HOW TO USE THIS BOOK

To help you find the details you need in this book, a quick and handy reference is provided by:

1. Index on page XVII-1
2. The chapters have different symbols for e
3. The contents pages start on page4
4. The glossary explains less familiar words on page XVI-1

AT RISK GROUPS

Important information for and about 'At risk groups' is highlighted in green and indicated throughout the book by the Family symbol shown here.

On the back cover you will find details of our freephone Foodline where we look forward to responding to your enquiries and concerns.

4

CONTENTS

Stars compained against 1980's

FOOD POISONING

Q: What is food poisoning?

A: Food poisoning is any disease of an infective or toxic nature caused by the consumption of food or water. Food intoxication may be caused by chemicals which occur naturally in certain plants and animals, or due to contamination from the environment. These forms of intoxication may sometimes produce similar effects to microbial food poisoning.

Q: What should you do if a member of the family is ill after eating something or if you believe you are a victim of an outbreak of food poisoning?

A: The first step should always be to contact your family doctor. He/she will be able to diagnose the problem and take any necessary action.

If food has an 'off' taste, smell or texture, it may indicate that bacteria are present in large numbers. Throw away any food that seems to be 'off'.

Unfortunately pathogenic bacteria ie. those producing harmful substances, may also be present when food does not appear 'off'. In general, the pathogens do not produce the changes mentioned above. As a guide throw away any food that is past its 'best before' or 'use by' date.

Q: What are the symptoms of food poisoning?

A: The symptoms vary depending on the type of bacteria. They often include nausea, headache, aching joints, vomiting and diarrhoea. Not all symptoms will necessarily be present.

The symptoms may appear almost instantaneously or there may be delay (incubation period). This depends on the type of bacteria causing the poisoning and how it works on the body. Some bacteria cause symptoms by infecting the intestines or the body, whereas others produce toxins (poisons) that cause the symptoms. If the incubation period is longer than two days it is often very difficult to trace the incident back to the food which caused the poisoning.

Q: Why has food poisoning suddenly become a problem?

A: The problem has always existed. We process food in an attempt to reduce the risk of food poisoning. For example, pasteurisation, cooking and canning are all safeguards against food poisoning.

In recent years the increase in the number of reported cases of food poisoning has resulted in increased awareness by consumers, the food industry and Government.

In a Government survey of domestic food handling practices carried out by the Ministry of Agriculture, Fisheries and Food in 1988, the results indicated that although the majority of consumers recognise some of the dangers associated with food handling, there seemed to be some confusion about the mechanisms of transmission of food poisoning.

The Government has taken several steps to improve legislation controlling the food industry, (The Food Safety Act 1990, the Food Hygiene Amendment Regulations 1990/91). As part of the food chain consumers must make every effort to always adopt the best food handling practices at home.

Q: Do other countries have a problem?

A: All Western countries have similar problems. There have been similar outbreaks in the USA and Europe caused by organisms like **Listeria monocytogenes** and **Salmonella**. The problem is even worse in lesser developed countries, where standards of preparation of food and sanitation facilities are poor.

Q: Who is responsible for ensuring food is safe?

A: Everyone has a responsibility to ensure that the food they handle is safe. This starts with the farmer and goes right through the food chain and includes the manufacturer, distributor, retailer and ultimately the consumer. Because consumers are last to handle food before it is eaten, they must be especially careful to ensure that the highest standards of hygiene and safety are maintained in its preparation, cooking and storage.

All forms of food poisoning are preventable and it is up to all those involved in different parts of the food chain to do all they can to prevent food poisoning.

By proper dissemination of information, and education we can ensure that every single person in the food chain is aware of their individual responsibility.

Q: How serious a problem is food poisoning?

A: There is a risk associated with everything we do and eating is no exception. We can reduce the risk by hygienically preparing and thoroughly cooking our food.

There are no exact figures for food poisoning because many cases go unreported. Other cases which have similar symptoms to food poisoning cannot always be positively traced back to food at all.

Each year between 1989 and 1992, about one in a thousand people suffered from reported cases of the two most common food poisoning bacteria, **Salmonella** and **Campylobacter jejuni**.

Q: How can food poisoning be prevented?

A: All forms of food poisoning are preventable. Food processing techniques are designed to prevent food poisoning and ensure food is as safe as possible. The best way to prevent it is to follow food handling practices, especially if you fall into one of the 'at risk' groups.

Q: Who are the 'at risk' groups?

A: Potentially anyone is at risk from the effects of food poisoning, although certain groups are more susceptible than others. These 'at risk' groups are:
▷ Babies and infants (under two years).
▷ Pregnant women and their unborn.
▷ Elderly people.
▷ Those who are already ill or are convalescing.
▷ Those who are taking drugs which suppress their body's natural ability to fight infection.
▷ Those on extensive treatment with antibiotics or receiving chemotherapy.
▷ Those with reduced natural ability to fight infection such as AIDS sufferers, alcoholics, drug abusers, diabetics and transplant patients.

If you are unsure whether or not you come into one of these groups you should contact your doctor. If you do not fall into an 'at risk' group there is no need to avoid any particular foods. However, everyone should ensure that the food they eat is bought from a reputable manufacturer or retailer, and is then hygienically stored and prepared. Everyone should follow the good food handling practices recommended on page II-1.

THE FOOD CHAIN

Farm inputs. Animal feed or Agrichemicals

The Farmer.

Slaughter House or Grain Store.

The Manufacturer.

Distributor & Transporter.

The Wholesaler.

Distributor & Transporter.

The Retailer.

Food Preparer.

The Consumer.

LISTERIA

Listeria are a group of bacteria some of which are potentially harmful to man, others are not. **Listeria monocytogenes** is the bacterium which is the most usual cause of the disease listeriosis in man and other animals.

The symptoms of listeriosis can range from a mild 'flu-like' symptom to premature birth or miscarriage in pregnant women, and meningitis in the newborn, young people or adults.

Q: Where does Listeria monocytogenes come from?

A: Listeria monocytogenes is widespread in the environment in every country of the world. It has been found in soil, dust, mud, vegetation, silage, sewage and is carried in the gut of many animals. Animals that carry **Listeria monocytogenes** are likely to infect the products they produce (milk) or those produced from them (meat). Up to five per cent or more of normal, healthy people carry **Listeria monocytogenes** in their gut and from there contaminate fingers, etc without showing any of the symptoms of listeriosis.

Good agricultural practices and hygienic preparation of food will reduce the level of **Listeria monocytogenes** present. The World Health Organisation (WHO) has stated that 'total elimination of **Listeria monocytogenes** from all foods is impractical and may even be impossible'. For this reason it is important to handle food materials safely and reduce the risk of contracting the disease.

Q: How is Listeriosis contracted?

A: The risk of a healthy person contracting listeriosis is small. Currently it is unclear why one person contracts listeriosis and while another carrying **Listeria monocytogenes** may show no signs of the disease. However, certain groups of people do appear to be more vulnerable than others. In the majority of cases the source of infection remains unknown but contaminated food has been directly implicated in a number of large outbreaks of the disease. For this reason, certain foods should be treated with caution, especially by those who fall into the 'at risk' groups. See page I-3.

Q: What foods should the 'at risk' groups avoid?

A: Avoid those foods which are potentially contaminated with **Listeria monocytogenes**, such as raw unpasteurised milk, or those that are most susceptible to the growth and multiplication of **Listeria monocytogenes** such as pâté and soft cheese. Although reputable food manufacturers make every effort to ensure that the food they produce is as hygienically prepared as possible, **Listeria monocytogenes** is present throughout the environment and can contaminate food and multiply even under chilled conditions.

DAIRY FOODS TO AVOID:

▷ **Unpasteurised (Green top) milk and products made with unpasteurised milk.** Cattle may not necessarily carry **Listeria monocytogenes** but if they do it can be passed on to the milk they produce and the milk may also be contaminated from environmental sources. Pasteurisation destroys any **Listeria monocytogenes** present. If the milk is not pasteurised the Listeria monocytogenes will, if present, continue to multiply.

▷ **Soft Mould Ripened Cheese**
Soft Mould Ripened Cheese – typically cheese with a white velvety rind such as Brie and Camembert or a blue veined such as Danish Blue. The process of pasteurisation, heats milk quickly to 72 degrees Celsius. The temperature is held for at least 15 seconds and then quickly cooled to less than 10 degrees Celsius. Milk for mould ripened cheese undergoes the heat treatment but not the cooling process. The milk is kept at about room temperature in order to allow the mould to multiply and ripen the cheese. If **Listeria monocytogenes** from the environment recontaminates the milk after the heat treatment it may also multiply in the cheese.

▷ **Ice Cream**
Ice Cream – soft whip ice cream from machines. Ice cream machines, if not thoroughly cleaned can potentially harbour **Listeria monocytogenes**. If the machine is not emptied when it is turned off, the fluctuation in temperature may allow **Listeria monocytogenes** to grow and multiply rapidly. Those in the 'at risk' groups should avoid ice cream from these machines.

WE ADVISE THAT NOBODY CONSUMES UNPASTEURISED (GREEN TOP) MILK

MEAT PRODUCTS TO AVOID

▷ **Pâté (Meat, Fish) and Vegetable Pâté**
Pâté from the deli-counter is susceptible to the growth of **Listeria monocytogenes** and should be avoided by those in the 'at risk' groups. Canned pâté or jars of paste (meat, fish) should be consumed within two days of opening and stored in the 'fridge once opened.

▷ Pre-cooked/ Ready Roast Poultry

Cold, ready cooked chicken and poultry should be avoided by those in the 'at risk' categories. **Listeria monocytogenes** has been identified as being present in a high percentage of these products and if the products are stored for any length of time the **Listeria monocytogenes** can grow and multiply. If you want to eat cold poultry, roast your own, cool it quickly and store it in the 'fridge for no longer than two days.

DAIRY FOODS THAT ARE CONSIDERED SAFE

▷ Pasteurised, sterilised and UHT milk

Pasteurised, sterilised and UHT milk – these treatments applied to milk will destroy **Listeria monocytogenes**. If milk is then properly stored, it will be safe to drink.

▷ Hard Cheese

Hard Cheese – such as Cheshire, Cheddar, Lancashire. **Listeria monocytogenes** does not grow readily in hard cheese because of the cheese's consistency and acidity. Those 'at risk' can safely eat hard cheeses. For those who are concerned about hard blue vein cheeses such as Stilton - there is still a risk but it is significantly reduced.

▷ Processed Soft Cheese

Processed Soft Cheese – although ripened soft cheese should be avoided, processed soft cheese such as cream cheese and cheese spreads are not considered a risk. The same applies to fromage frais, cottage cheese, and yoghurt. These products have high acid content and, although the acid does not kill **Listeria monocytogenes** it will prevent its growth and multiplication.

▷ Block Ice Cream

Ice cream – bought in either a block form or as a preformed cone or lolly, produced by a manufacturer, will be acceptable. Ice cream of this type will have undergone quality control procedures by the manufacturer and often by the retailer. It must be fit for consumption before it is released for sale.

MEAT PRODUCTS THAT ARE CONSIDERED SAFE

▷ If hygienically prepared, cold meats can be eaten safely. If you are at all concerned about the standard of hygiene used in the preparation of a cold meat you would be best advised to avoid it. Fermented and dehydrated meat products such as salami are safe as there is not enough available water in the food for **Listeria monocytogenes** to grow.

▷ Canned pâté and jars of paste (meat, fish) are also safe. These products undergo a heat treatment which destroys the **Listeria monocytogenes**. Once opened they should be stored in a loosely covered container in the 'fridge and consumed within two days.

HANDLING SALADS AND VEGETABLES

Prepared salads, the sort you can buy in supermarkets, are not a high risk food if hygienically prepared and stored for a short time under refrigerated conditions.

However, in a small number of cases, prepared salads have been implicated as sources of **Listeria monocytogenes**. If possible wash the salad in cold, running water before eating. The safest way to be sure a salad is safe is to prepare it yourself. Washing the salad vegetables thoroughly in cold running water will remove any soil or other dirt. Do not wash different vegetables in the same water, as this may wash dirt and micro-organisms off one vegetable onto the next.

HANDLING COOK-CHILL MEALS

The term 'cook-chill', as the name suggests, refers to food that has been cooked and subsequently stored under refrigerated conditions to be reheated and served at a later stage. Although cook-chill is normally applied to ready to eat meals and TV dinners bought from shops or some restaurants, it also covers leftovers from meals prepared at home to be eaten later.

Listeria monocytogenes is killed at temperatures above 70 degrees Celsius. If the food is thoroughly reheated so that it is piping hot right through to the centre, **Listeria monocytogenes** will not survive. There is no need for those in the 'at risk' categories to avoid cook-chill foods but they should handle them properly as directed by the manufacturer. Only heat them once and do not consume them after the use by date.

Q: Should mothers who are breast feeding avoid the above foods?

A: No case of human listerial mastitis has ever been reported. It is important that the mother of a newly-born baby observes a particularly strict standard of hygiene when handling food, more for her baby's sake than her own. Once the baby is born the mother is no longer in the 'at risk' category but her baby is.

Q: What good food handling practices can everyone follow to reduce the risk of food poisoning?

A: Follow the good food handling practices recommended in Chapter II. The key points to remember are:

▷ Check the temperature of your fridge. The colder it is the slower the growth of micro-organisms and the safer the food. (See chapter IV).
▷ Refrigerate perishable foods as soon as possible.
▷ Cool leftovers and refrigerate within one hour of preparation.
▷ Re-heat food until it is piping hot.
▷ Only ever re-heat food once. Throw away whatever is not eaten.
▷ Take care to avoid contact between cooked or ready-to-eat and raw food.
▷ Store food in clean dry containers.
▷ Wash hands, kitchen surfaces and utensils with detergent and water, then dry thoroughly.
▷ Chopping boards should be thoroughly scrubbed.
▷ Change and wash tea towels and dish-cloths every day.
▷ Keep animals out of the kitchen or at least off the work surfaces.
▷ Check for weevils, insects and kitchen pests.
▷ Never sort out dirty washing on kitchen work surfaces.
▷ Always wash your hands after handling dirty washing.
▷ Keep your kitchen clean.
▷ Always wash your hands after handling rubbish.

Q: Are microwave ovens and slow cookers safe to cook in?

A: Provided they are functioning correctly, there is no risk from using microwave ovens or slow cookers. Check the slow cooker is capable of attaining a temperature of at least 70 degrees Celsius by using a food thermometer. If you are in any doubt have your cooker serviced.

It is important to observe standing times when cooking food in a microwave oven. Follow the recommendations in your microwave oven manufacturer's handbook or refer to Chapter III. The chances of fit, healthy adults contracting listeriosis are very slim. There is no need for them to alter their diet. Listeriosis, like all other forms of food poisoning is preventable, provided good food handling practices are followed.

SALMONELLA

Salmonella are a group of bacteria that can multiply rapidly in food if measures are not taken to prevent it.

There are many kinds of **Salmonella**, nearly all of which can cause illness, including food borne gastroenteritis in humans. **Salmonella** infections have been recognised for a long time as a common cause of food poisoning all over the world.

Q: What are the symptoms of Salmonella food poisoning?

A: Salmonella gastroenteritis can cause a variety of symptoms from nausea and abdominal pain to fever, diarrhoea and sometimes vomiting. Symptoms usually begin 12-36 hours after eating contaminated food.

The length of the illness can vary, but it normally lasts for at least two or three days. It is possible to become a carrier of **Salmonella** even after the symptoms have disappeared. You can also be a carrier without showing the symptoms. If you have been part of a food poisoning outbreak, for example if you have attended a dinner where other guests have later become ill, contact your doctor.

Q: How can Salmonella be avoided?

A: Salmonella gastroenteritis like all forms of food borne illness is preventable by following the good food handling practices recommended in chapter 2.

Salmonella is killed when food is properly cooked. Food should always be cooked or reheated until it is piping hot (over 70 degrees Celsius throughout).

Most cases of **Salmonella** gastroenteritis can be traced to uncooked or badly cooked foods or food that has been cooked and recontaminated. For example, if an egg custard pie is cut with a knife that has been used for raw meat and not been thoroughly washed then contamination can occur. If a member of the family or someone you are nursing is suffering from **Salmonella** gastroenteritis you should be especially careful when preparing food. Wash your hands thoroughly after contact with the infected person.

Q: Which foods contain Salmonella?

A: The foods most commonly susceptible to **Salmonella** contamination are meat and meat products, poultry, eggs, milk and milk products. If these are properly prepared they do not pose a risk.

Q: Are eggs safe to eat?

A: Yes. Hard cooked eggs are safe for everyone if properly stored and prepared. Eating raw eggs is not recommended. Only those in the 'at risk' groups need to avoid lightly cooked eggs and egg dishes.

A healthy, fit person need not worry about eating eggs providing they observe the recommendations on storage and preparation set out below.

Q: How should eggs be stored and prepared?

A: It is not recommended that anyone should eat raw eggs. In order to ensure your eggs are as safe as possible follow the recommendations below.

▷ Always buy eggs from a reputable supplier, who has a good turnover. If the supplier sells a lot of eggs, they are more likely to be fresh.

▷ Check the date mark on the packet.

▷ Store eggs in a refrigerator.

▷ Never store eggs in a warm room or a room that fluctuates in temperature as this can lead to any bacteria present multiplying at a rapid rate.

▷ Use eggs within two weeks of purchase.

▷ Never use a cracked or damaged egg.

▷ If an egg is dirty, wipe it clean with a clean dry cloth, preferably a disposable kitchen towel. If it is still dirty leave it until you are about to use it, then wash it in warm water and dry. Once washed, eggs should not be stored, since washing destroys the protective film on the egg shell making it more permeable.

▷ Once cooked, hard boiled eggs should not be returned to their original container. If you wish to store hard boiled eggs, do so in a clean dry bowl with a lid.

Q: How should those in the 'at risk' categories prepare eggs?

A: Those in the 'at risk' categories should avoid raw eggs and dishes that contain raw eggs. To be completely certain do not eat lightly cooked eggs or dishes that contain lightly cooked eggs, since their internal temperature does not reach the point at which any **Salmonella** present would be destroyed.

▷ Eggs to be hard boiled, should be cooked for at least seven minutes.

▷ Eggs to be fried, should be cooked for three minutes on each side.

▷ Eggs for scrambling should be cooked until they have a solid and firm texture.

The following home-made dishes should be avoided if prepared with unpasteurised eggs: Mayonnaise, Egg Custard/Egg Nog, Hollandaise Sauce, Ice Cream/Soufflé, Royal icing/other icing containing eggs. Meringues must be cooked thoroughly until dry in the centre.

Most commercially prepared foods of the above type are made using pasteurised eggs and therefore do not present a risk. If in doubt, check with the manufacturer whose address should be on the product label.

There are a number of brands of pasteurised egg on the market which you can use if you are particularly concerned about the safety of whole eggs. They come in either UHT, frozen or dried form. Use as soon as opened, or when prepared, within two days.

A: Milk
Apart from green top (unpasteurised) milk, other milk and many milk products are heat treated before we buy them. Pasteurised and long life milk can be used straight from the bottle or the carton.

Meat and poultry
Meat and poultry pose a risk if they are not thoroughly cooked. Follow the guidelines in the good food handling practices, chapter 2, and the recommended cooking times in following chapters.

OTHER BACTERIA:

CAMPYLOBACTER

There are many types of **Campylobacter** spp. **Campylobacter jejuni** is the most frequent cause of diarrhoea in Britain. **Campylobacter** diarrhoea is generally considered to be a food borne or water borne infection rather than food poisoning. If these bacteria are present in food they do not tend to multiply in it. However, once swallowed the bacteria can multiply in the gut causing infection. These bacteria need a nutritionally rich medium and a low oxygen atmosphere to grow. They survive well in a moist, cool environment but are easily killed by mild heating.

Q: What are the symptoms?

A: The symptoms of campylobacteriosis begin between one to seven days after infection. Fever, headache and aching muscles are followed by diarrhoea, abdominal pain and fever. The illness usually lasts from one to four days and although very unpleasant is seldom serious. Treatment is not normally necessary, apart from rest, and drinking plenty of fluids. There is an effective antibiotic treatment for complicated or unusually severe cases.

Q: Sources of infection?

A: Human **Campylobacter** infections are thought to occur mainly via food, milk or water. The following precautions can greatly reduce the incidence of **Campylobacter diarrhoea.**
1. Do not drink raw milk, which is not pasteurised, sterilised or ultra heat treated (UHT).
2. Do not drink water from an un-chlorinated supply or directly from a well that has not been checked to see that it is free from faecal pollution.

3. Avoid cross-contamination between raw food and cooked food, or food that will be eaten cold. Be especially careful when handling raw chicken, raw offal and other raw meat.

CLOSTRIDIUM BOTULINUM 1993.
2007 CALLED CLOSTRIDIUM DIFFICILE

Botulism is a very severe form of food poisoning caused by a toxin produced by the bacterium known as Clostridium botulinum.

Q: What is Clostridium botulinum?

A: Clostridium botulinum is a bacterium commonly found in soil. It is a spore-forming bacterium which means that even when the live bacteria are killed the next generation is present in a dormant form, known as a spore. Fortunately, the spores need specific conditions in order to be able to germinate, and having germinated, a different set of conditions are required for growth. Food processing methods are designed specifically to reduce any risk of botulism food poisoning.

Q: How serious a problem is botulism?

A: If food is properly processed so that all the **Clostridium botulinum** spores present are killed, no risk arises.

Botulism is very rare in the UK. Most cases in the past have resulted from badly processed foods or damaged containers. Botulism is a greater problem in countries where home preserving, such as bottling and canning, is popular. In developed countries most reported cases occur in the USA. The most recent botulism outbreak in the UK was in 1989 with hazelnut yoghurt. The source was linked to the hazelnut puree, which is believed to have been badly processed.

Q: What are the symptoms of botulism?

A: Botulism causes difficulties in swallowing, talking, breathing, and induces blurred or double vision. Botulism toxin is probably the most poisonous substance known to man. Symptoms occur usually between 12 and 36 hours after eating but can appear from two hours to even eight days later. Death can often result because of respiratory or cardiac failure. However, if quick action is taken by administering an antitoxin, the victim can be saved.

Q: What foods are most risky?

A: The rare instances of botulism usually occur as a result of eating foods that have been badly processed and/or not thoroughly reheated before they are eaten. If food is properly processed **Clostridium botulinum** will not be capable of producing its harmful toxin. The toxin is destroyed by heat at 80 degrees Celsius for 10 minutes.

▷ Avoid cross-contamination eg. from soiled food such as fresh vegetables to other foods.

▷ Avoid cans or vacuum packs which have 'blown'.

▷ Avoid dented or rusty cans; check the seams on cans and vacuum packs.

▷ Prepare raw fish well, making sure it is properly gutted and cleaned.

ESCHERICHIA COLI

Escherichia coli is a bacterium naturally found in the intestines of man and animals. Only certain strains of **E.coli** are known to cause food poisoning.

Q: What are the symptoms of E.Coli food poisoning?

A: E.coli causes illness usually within 12 to 24 hours but sometimes up to 72 hours after eating. The symptoms are abdominal pains, fever, diarrhoea and vomiting. The symptoms are caused by the bacteria multiplying in the intestine and producing toxins. The illness lasts from one to seven days. If you are concerned that you may be infected, it would be advisable to consult your doctor.

Q: How can E.Coli be avoided?

A: Contamination is caused by the transfer of **E.coli** from faeces to food. Good personal hygiene such as thoroughly washing hands, scrubbing nails and drying hands on a clean towel after going to the lavatory, can help prevent the spread of **E.coli**. Meat can be contaminated with **E.coli**. This may be as a result of poor handling where the animal or other animals faeces may have infected the raw meat.

Q: Which foods are the most susceptible?

A: The foods that are most susceptible are those which are handled frequently, for example, cold foods such as sandwiches, salads and undercooked foods such as beefburgers and barbecued chicken. If you are buying snack foods check the hygiene of the outlet if possible and the 'use by' date or 'best before' date on the product. If you are in any doubt, do not buy.

STAPHYLOCOCCUS AUREUS

The organism that causes staphylococcal food poisoning is known as **Staphylococcus aureus**. This bacterium is commonly found in the nasal passages of humans and animals and can be often found in infected wounds or boils. An

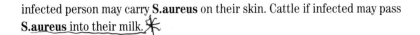

infected person may carry **S.aureus** on their skin. Cattle if infected may pass **S.aureus** into their milk.

Q: What are the symptoms?

A: Different individuals differ in susceptibility to staphylococcal poisoning. The toxin produced by **S.aureus** normally takes effect within 1 to 4 hours of eating but can take as long as seven hours. The symptoms are salivation, nausea, vomiting, abdominal cramps and diarrhoea. Recovery is normally within two days.

Q: How can staphylococcus poisoning be prevented?

A: Good food handling practices should be observed. Those involved in food preparation must be especially careful with cuts and wounds. These should be covered with a clean waterproof dressing.

Hygienic preparation and thorough cooking of food will prevent it from becoming contaminated with the bacterium. However, if contamination has taken place and the bacteria have produced toxins, these toxins will not be destroyed by reheating. For this reason prevention is all important.

Q: What foods are susceptible?   *CAN CHANGE INTO DIFFERENT.*
SORT OF   BACTERIA ; ORGANISM!

A: Many kinds of food have been involved with staphylococcal food poisoning, including poultry, fish, meat, milk and related products. Special care should be taken with cream, custards and sauces and any baked food containing cream. These are ideal foods for the growth of **S.aureus.**

BACILLUS CEREUS

Bacillus cereus is another food poisoning bacterium that deserves a special mention. These bacteria are common in soil but if present in food can produce a toxin. The toxin can lead to nausea, abdominal cramps, diarrhoea or vomiting.

Q: How soon after eating the food will you be affected?

A: If the food you eat contains toxins you will be affected very quickly. Usually the incubation period is 1 to 6 hours for vomiting symptoms, 8 to 16 hours for diarrhoea.

Q: What foods are most likely to be affected?

A: Boiled rice and fried rice are common sources of this toxin, particularly if bulk quantities have been cooked and left to stand for some time at normal room temperature. Custards, cereal products, puddings and sauces may also be affected.

Q: How can intoxication be avoided?

A: Always chill foods rapidly. If food has been prepared in bulk, separate into smaller quantities and place in clean containers to allow quicker cooling.
▷ Store food at less than 5 degrees Celsius in a refrigerator.
▷ Reheat food thoroughly to above 70 degrees Celsius.
▷ Always follow the good food handling practices recommended for hygienic preparation of foods.

MOULDS

Moulds belong to a group of organisms known as fungi. Moulds often look like fuzzy, cotton wool. The majority are white but some appear smokey, dark or coloured. While many moulds result in the spoilage of food, some may produce toxic metabolites (mycotoxins) which are harmful when eaten. Others, such as mushrooms, are eaten as foods. Some may have useful characteristics that can be used in the production of foods, such as miso, soy sauce, Camembert, blue cheeses and amylase (which is used in the production of bread).

Q: What enables a mould to grow?

A: Moulds require moisture and a suitable substance to feed on. Moulds require less moisture for growth than most bacteria and yeasts. The presence of mould is often a useful indication that the food may have other micro-organisms present, (with the exception of most jams which are too acid for bacteria to survive in). Mouldy food should be thrown away. It is not enough to scrape off the visible mould as both mould and any toxins that have been produced may still be present in other parts of the food.

Q: Where can moulds be found?

A: Moulds can be found on any suitable nutrient base, providing there is sufficient moisture. Moulds can grow over a wide range of temperatures. Most moulds thrive at room temperature but a few can grow at refrigerated temperatures. CHEESE

Q: How do moulds spread?

A: Moulds reproduce by forming spores which are released into the air. If the spores fall into a favourable environment, for example moist food, they germinate and grow, producing a new colony.

Q: What steps can be taken to prevent mould contamination?

A: Keep food covered and always replace the original lid on a jar as soon as you have used it.

▷ If the refrigerator contains mould, wash the 'fridge thoroughly and then dry. Check the temperature which should be between 0 and 5 degrees Celsius.

▷ Never put hot food straight into the refrigerator. Allow food to cool before refrigeration, as warm food encourages condensation and heats up the refrigerator.

▷ Clean the refrigerator and work surfaces regularly with mild disinfectant solution, (a detergent and water would be suitable).

▷ Always store food in clean, dry containers.

▷ If food 'sweats' in its container, remove it and place in a more suitable one.

▷ Avoid storing food in humid environments. A cool, dry cupboard is recommended for dried foods.

Q: What are mycotoxins?

A: Mycotoxins are toxic substances produced in minute quantities by moulds for example aflatoxin and patulin. *A F LATOXIN — Peanuts — Bird food. — Garden.*

Q: Is there any relationship between mould on dried figs and nuts and cancer of the liver?

A: Some moulds can produce a toxin known as aflatoxin, which has been shown to induce cancer of the liver in animals. Aflatoxin poisoning has been reported in less-developed countries where dry foods are badly stored.

Stringent quality control tests eliminate the risk of badly stored dried figs and nuts being imported into this country. All such imports must be accompanied by certification showing that they have been tested and cleared for consumption.

Q: How common is aflatoxin poisoning?

A: There have been no recorded deaths in the United Kingdom or Europe. Deaths have occurred in India where nuts are stored on the ground.

Q: How can aflatoxins be avoided?

A: Avoid buying any food that is mouldy or that you suspect has been mishandled. Always buy from a reputable retailer. Both UK manufacturers and UK retailers check that nuts and dried fruit are safe for human consumption.

Throw away any food that appears mouldy. Cooking mouldy food does not make it safe to eat. This is because toxins produced by the mould are not destroyed at high temperatures, even though the mould may have been destroyed.

PARASITES IN FOOD

Parasites are organisms that obtain their food from another living organism (the host) to the detriment of the host. One example of a food borne parasite is **Toxoplasma gondii** which is the cause of the disease Toxoplasmosis.

Q: What is toxoplasmosis?

A: Toxoplasmosis is a disease that occurs worldwide in both humans and animals. It is caused by a single celled micro-organism known as **Toxoplasma gondii**, and is neither a bacterium nor a virus. Although many people may be infected, most do not show any signs of the disease. Infection is most hazardous to those in the 'at risk' groups.

Q: How is toxoplasmosis spread?

A: The parasite is spread to humans via undercooked and raw meat. Vegetables contaminated with infected cat faeces and cat litter are possible sources of infection. Although **Toxoplasma gondii** is commonly found in many animals it is only in the cat's gut that the male and female parasite join to produce an infective form. If these forms are swallowed by someone in the 'at risk' groups, infection can occur. For this reason it is important to wash your hands thoroughly after handling cats or cat litter.

Q: What are the symptoms of toxoplasmosis?

A: Most infections produce either no symptoms or mild aches and pains and a slightly raised temperature. Swollen lymph glands may also occur.

Q: How can toxoplasmosis be prevented?

A: Wash all fruit and vegetables thoroughly, especially if you grow your own fruit and vegetables, or if you or your neighbours keep pets.
▷ Pregnant women should not eat raw or undercooked meat.
▷ Pregnant women should avoid handling cat litter, cat faeces and any soil that is potentially contaminated with faeces.

▷ Keep domestic pets off the work surfaces or, where possible, out of the kitchen.
▷ Wash hands thoroughly before eating and, before and after preparing food.
▷ You should wash your hands after contact with cat litter and soil, and after handling pets.

Q: How common is toxoplasmosis?

A: The risk of contracting toxoplasmosis is small. It has been estimated that in the United Kingdom approximately 0.5% to 1% of the population contract the infection each year. Not all of these will show any symptoms. About 12 severe infections in children are reported each year, but this may well be an underestimate. For this reason it is wise for those in the 'at risk' categories to take note of the above precautions.

NATURAL TOXINS IN FOOD

Some foods naturally contain poisons which may present a risk to our health. These poisons are referred to as 'toxins'.

Toxicologists - those who study poisons - have established that the main risk from carcinogens (poisons that produce cancers) in the diet come from natural carcinogens in food as opposed to additives or pesticide residues. A number of foods contain toxins that if eaten in excess affect the body's normal functions. Examples of these are:

▷ Oxalic Acid – which is found in a number of vegetables such as rhubarb and spinach.
▷ Solanine – which is found in green or sprouting potatoes. ✷
▷ Haemagglutinin – which is found in red kidney beans.   HAEMA. = BLOOD

SOLANINE IN POTATOES

Q: Are green or sprouting potatoes safe to eat?

A: The Food Safety Advisory Centre (FSAC) would not advise you to eat green or sprouting potatoes. The toxin Solanine builds up in the potato once it starts sprouting. When the toxin is present in large amounts a distinctive bitter taste can be detected. It is not enough to peel off the green portion, because although Solanine is usually concentrated near the outside of the potato, it can run right through the potato. The symptoms are initially gastro-intestinal discomfort, which may lead to diarrhoea and could ultimately be fatal.

Q: How can you avoid green and sprouting potatoes?

A: The FSAC suggests that you select potatoes that are not green. Buy them in quantities that can be consumed fairly swiftly.

Potatoes should be stored in a cool, dry, dark place. Potatoes will turn green if exposed to light for more than a few days. If you have bought a large number of potatoes which are noticeably green before storage, you would be advised to return them to the shop from which they were purchased.

HAEMAGGLUTININ IN RED KIDNEY BEANS

Q: Are red kidney beans safe to eat?

A: Red kidney beans contain a protein called haemagglutinin, which if not destroyed during cooking, when consumed may cause red blood cells to mass together. Thorough cooking of the beans will destroy the protein structure and prevent this.

Q: How can you ensure red kidney beans are thoroughly cooked?

A: Red kidney beans should be cooked as follows: Soak the beans overnight if required. Rinse them and boil rapidly in fresh water for 10 minutes. Drain and rinse with either hot or cold water. Cover the beans with water. Bring to the boil and simmer until the beans reach the desired texture. If cooking the beans in a slow-cooker, boil separately for 10 minutes prior to the cooking. The slow cooker, though it will cook the beans, does not heat them sufficiently.

Q: Do other pulses require the same cooking procedure?

A: Soya beans also contain similar toxins and should be cooked in the same way as above. Other pulses do not need to be pre-boiled.

OXALIC ACID IN RHUBARB

Q: Is rhubarb poisonous?

A: There are several natural toxins present in rhubarb, one of which is oxalic acid. There is however more oxalic acid present in the leaf of the plant than in the stem.

If you suffer from kidney stones, which are formed from calcium oxalate, it is advisable to avoid rhubarb and spinach. However, both rhubarb and spinach are good sources of fibre and may help to provide a balanced diet.

Q: Does rhubarb affect calcium absorption?

A: Yes. The oxalic acid in rhubarb when mixed with calcium in other foods forms an insoluble salt. Eating rhubarb will reduce but not completely block calcium absorption. Rhubarb also has a laxative effect.

If you are eating too much rhubarb, you will have a stomach upset to warn you to cut down. Eating a reasonable amount of rhubarb once or twice a week will not adversely affect your health.

Q: Is oxalic acid destroyed by cooking?

A: No. Oxalic acid is heat stable and will not be destroyed by cooking.

PATULIN

Q: What is Patulin?

A: Patulin is a mycotoxin found in fruit that has been affected by mould.

Q: How does Patulin get into fruit?

A: If fruit has been badly bruised, the damage makes it highly vulnerable to attack by micro-organisms such as mould. If the fruit is stored for any length of time, some of the mould growing may produce toxins such as Patulin.

Q: Which foods are vulnerable to this mould attack?

A: Soft fruits such as apples, pears, cherries, apricots and peaches are vulnerable to attack by moulds capable of producing Patulin.

Q: How can Patulin get into apple juice?

A: If apples have been stored for a long period there is a chance that any bruised apples may have been attacked by mould. Some apple varieties also exhibit core rot which can only be detected by cutting the apple open. If these apples are pulped for juice any bad apple will affect the quality of the juice.

Q: What can consumers do to safeguard their supply?

A: Even if just a few bruised apples are pulped they will contaminate the rest of the juice. For this reason it is important to choose your juice from a reputable supplier. Reputable manufacturers and retailers who wish to observe **due diligence** in respect of the Food Safety Act 1990 should routinely test apples prior to pulping and only offer for sale juice that falls within permitted limits.

Q: What are the permitted limits?

A: The World Health Organisation (WHO) has established a safety standard for patulin in apple juice of 50 parts per billion (ppb).

Q: How should you prepare fruit juice at home?

A: If you are producing juice from your own fruit at home ensure that the fruit is in good condition. Wash the fruit thoroughly in cold running water. Damaged or bruised fruit should not be used particularly if there is any evidence of mould growth. Any fruit contaminated by mould should be discarded. Drink the juice immediately, or store in the 'fridge. Consume the juice within 24 hours of preparation. Adding a little lemon juice will prevent the juice from browning.

GOOD FOOD HANDLING PRACTICE

Buy from a reputable retailer with good hygiene standards. Look for stores that are well lit, well organised and obviously clean, for example, with no spillages in the food cabinets or on the floor. Look for cleanliness and helpfulness of staff. Staff handling food, for example, those behind the delicatessen, butchery, bakery and fishmonger counters, should conform to food hygiene regulations.

▷ Staff should have clean overalls.

▷ Jewellery should be kept to a minimum.

▷ Hair should be tied back and covered; Fingernails should be short and clean.

▷ Staff should be free from coughs, colds and other infections.

▷ Any cuts should be covered with a food standard (usually blue) waterproof dressing.

▷ Staff should have gloves, tongs and/or paper to keep their hands away from the food.

The following facilities should be close by:

▷ Wash hand basin

▷ A separate slicer and separate small utensils for raw and cooked products.

Avoid buying food in damaged containers.

Scrutinise the 'use-by' date and the 'best before' dates of food. These dates tell you when food is best. Do not buy food that has passed the date shown.

Highly perishable items which need refrigeration should always be sold from refrigerated cabinets even if the food is on special offer and a quick sale is anticipated.

Frozen food should not be stacked above the load line in the freezer units. If it is, report it to customer services or a senior member of staff. If you have a lot of shopping to do, select chilled and frozen food last as this will minimise the amount of time during which the food can heat up.

Produce such as fruit and vegetables, plants and flowers should be kept in separate areas. Loose produce in particular could have soil and soil organisms attached. They should be stored away from fish, meat, dairy and delicatessen items, both in the store and at home and so avoid any cross-contamination.

Every effort should be made to prevent cross-contamination, (the movement of micro-organisms from one distinct item to another) for example, from soil on vegetables to delicatessen products, or from meat to cheese. Cross-contamination can also take place via a vector ie. from meat to chopping board to cheese.

Different products should be stored in different areas, for example, cheese should not come into direct contact with meat or surfaces where meat has been prepared.

At the checkout, queues should not be allowed to build up; bags should be provided for the separation of frozen and chilled foods. Once you leave the store you should take food home as quickly as possible. Put chilled and frozen food straight into the refrigerator or freezer.

IN THE KITCHEN

Good kitchen hygiene requires organisation. The following guidelines are recommended for handling food.

▷ Get the shopping home as quickly as possible. Chilled and frozen food should go straight into the refrigerator or freezer. If you have a long journey from the store to home put food into an insulated cool bag or a cardboard box lined with newspaper.

▷ Check your refrigerator and freezer are working correctly and that food is stored properly - follow the guidelines given in Chapter IV. If food is not correctly stored its shelf life can be reduced dramatically.

▷ When handling food make sure your hands are clean.

▷ Wash your hands between handling raw foods and cooked or ready to eat foods. Use a clean towel.

▷ You should try to keep domestic pets out of the kitchen. Animals can carry bacteria and dirt from paws and air-borne fur can contaminate kitchen surfaces.

▷ Work surfaces need to be washed thoroughly, as does the inside of the fridge. Although they might look clean, surfaces can still be contaminated with bacteria which are too small to be seen. Dry work surfaces with a clean dry cloth; wet surfaces are a potential breeding ground for bacteria.

▷ Cutting and chopping boards need special attention as they can be the cause of the transfer of infection from one kind of food to another. Chopping boards should be thoroughly scrubbed with detergent. Wooden boards, which are porous and can harbour bacteria, should be scraped with a sharp knife from time to time. Plastic polyboards are much safer as they can be steeped in hot water.

▷ Just as you should wash your hands between preparing raw foods and cooked foods it is equally important to wash the knives and other utensils that you are using.

▷ Do not put cooked or ready to eat foods onto a surface which has just had raw food on it. Raw food, especially meat and fish, is far more likely than cooked food to have bacteria on it.

▷ Never add fresh food to unwashed containers.

▷ Do not reuse old polythene bags or food wrappings such as foil or cling film.

▷ Always wash fruit, vegetables and salad in clean, cold, running water.

▷ Check little-used cupboards for weevils and insects. If there are weevils and insects in the kitchen get rid of them immediately. If the problem persists, your local council may be able to help or advise you.

▷ Do not smoke whilst preparing food.

▷ If you cut yourself, cover the wound with a sterile waterproof dressing.

▷ Change and wash tea towels and dishcloths daily; otherwise bacteria can start to build up and contaminate surfaces with which the cloth comes into contact.

▷ Keep the kitchen bin, especially the lid, clean. Handling a dirty lid can spread bacteria and bins without lids can encourage flies which spread bacteria. Wash and dry the bin before putting in a new liner bag. Always wash your hands after handling rubbish.

▷ Be especially careful after handling domestic washing. Never sort out soiled washing on surfaces where food is prepared. Soiled washing can spread bacteria especially if a member of the family has an infection or is suffering from diarrhoea. Always wash your hands after handling washing.

PEST CONTROL IN THE KITCHEN

Once you have discovered a pest in the kitchen it is important to eradicate it as soon as possible. There are three methods of doing this.

1. Contact the local Environmental Health Department. You can do this via your local council offices. They normally deal with rodents such as mice and rats or with insects that can be considered a threat to public health such as wasps.

2. Call in a private pest control association. You will find them listed under 'pest control' in the Yellow Pages.

3. Deal with the problem yourself by buying suitable pesticide products from your local hardware store, chemist or supermarket.
   Take care with these products and follow the instructions carefully.

PRINCIPLE RULES TO FOLLOW TO PREVENT PEST INFESTATION

1. Cover fresh food.
2. Keep all surfaces clean and crumb free.
3. Check little used cupboards and clean behind furniture.
4. Ensure jars with lids and containers with tops are securely closed.
5. Shut waste bins tightly and put rubbish out often.
6. Do not neglect household maintenance. Gaps around woodwork and brickwork can encourage insects to nest.

AN EXAMPLE OF HOW INFECTION CAN TAKE PLACE DUE TO MIS-HANDLING OF FOOD

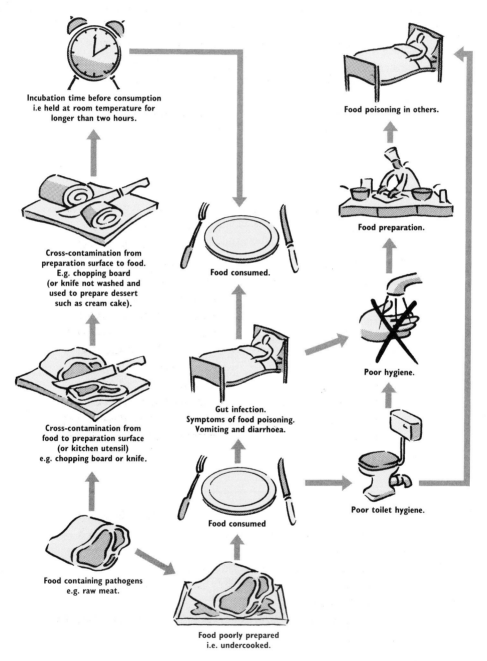

Incubation time before consumption i.e held at room temperature for longer than two hours.

Cross-contamination from preparation surface to food. E.g. chopping board (or knife not washed and used to prepare dessert such as cream cake).

Cross-contamination from food to preparation surface (or kitchen utensil) e.g. chopping board or knife.

Food containing pathogens e.g. raw meat.

Food consumed.

Food poisoning in others.

Food preparation.

Poor hygiene.

Gut infection. Symptoms of food poisoning. Vomiting and diarrhoea.

Poor toilet hygiene.

Food consumed

Food poorly prepared i.e. undercooked.

USE OF INSECTICIDES

Most products are specific for certain groups of pests eg. flying insects, crawling insects. The product label will advise you of its particular use. Most products are not toxic to humans. However, do not assume this. Although they may not be toxic, they will almost certainly be unpleasant or be an irritant, so avoid spraying them near food preparation surfaces or on soft furnishings. It is important to keep all pesticides out of the reach of children, make sure they are clearly marked and keep them in their original container. If there are asthmatics or bronchial sufferers in the house avoid using the sprays in their presence.

Q: What are flour mites?

A: Flour mites are common in the home and can be found living in flour or in the seal at the top of the flour bag. Sometimes they can be present in other food or on dried goods, or in paper. They are sometimes called Book Lice. They are often found in new kitchen units or between the shelves and sides of kitchen units, especially if the unit is made of chipboard. Mites can also live between wallpaper and plaster in old houses. Mites like warm, humid and dark conditions. They are not easy to eradicate, and there is often re-infection after cleaning, even if an insecticide is used. Storing food in clean, dry, glass containers with an airtight rubber seal is the best way to exclude them from food. If the property is old and centrally heated, any infection by flour mites may be due to damaged plaster or poor decoration. They are not present as the result of unhygienic conditions. We would recommend using an ammonia-based cleaner. If the problem persists or is very serious, contact a Hygiene and Pest Control company. If flour mites are found in a recently purchased bag of flour, or other dry ingredients, wrap the packet up well and return it to the shop. Check the cupboard for any contamination that may have occurred. Ammonia is a very very toxic product

COOKING

▷ Read and follow the thawing and cooking instructions on frozen foods very carefully. It is particularly important that meat and poultry are completely thawed before cooking.

▷ A guide to thawing times can be found on page IV-13.

▷ Do not re-freeze foods once thawed unless they have been thoroughly cooked.

▷ Always cook food thoroughly.

▷ Follow the cooking instructions and make sure that the food is really piping hot at the centre.

▷ If you are cooking in a microwave oven, observe the standing times recommended by the manufacturer. If food is not piping hot throughout bacteria may still be present.

▷ Cool leftover food quickly and put it into the refrigerator or freezer as soon as it is cool.

▷ Do not leave perishable food out at room temperature for more than one hour.

▷ Only re-heat cooked food once, whether originally cooked in your kitchen or purchased as a cook-chill product. Throw away any left overs after the first reheating. Food that is repeatedly heated is less appetising, less nutritious and also less safe. If food is not thoroughly reheated until it is piping hot bacteria and any toxins they produce can survive. If the warm food is then stored the bacteria can multiply to dangerous levels and possibly produce toxins. These toxins may well be stable even when the food is next reheated.

▷ During heating, make sure food reaches an internal temperature of 70 degrees Celsius for a minimum of 2 minutes. It is better to heat food until it is too hot and allow it to cool than to under cook or under-heat food.

▷ If food is not thoroughly reheated any bacteria that have reinfected the food after the initial cooking can survive and multiply.

▷ Only by thoroughly re-heating the food until it is piping hot can these bacteria be destroyed. However if bacteria such as **Staphylococcus aureus** have multiplied they may have formed heat resistant toxin and so the food may still be unsafe.

▷ The effects of food poisoning are discussed in Chapter I. Different cooking methods will be discussed later in this chapter.

ALL COOKING INSTRUCTIONS IN THIS BOOK REFER TO FRESH OR DEFROSTED PRODUCE.

CONVENTIONAL COOKING

Cooking food is a very effective method of both destroying any dangerous bacteria present and improving the taste, smell, texture and appearance of food. There are many different cooking methods: pressure cooking, microwaving and the more conventional cooking methods. Conventional cooking can be sub-divided into dry and wet methods. Cooking in fat is sometimes referred to as a dry cooking method.

Dry methods:	Hot fat methods:	Wet methods:
roasting	deep frying	boiling
baking	shallow frying	steaming
grilling	sauteing	poaching
	stir-frying	casseroling

The cooking method chosen depends on the nature of the ingredients. Some foods such as potatoes can be cooked by most of the methods mentioned above. Other foods may be more delicate or require special preparation. Red kidney beans, for example, require soaking followed by thorough boiling in order to destroy naturally-occurring toxins. Once prepared they can be cooked by some of the other methods mentioned above. The following section gives general guidelines to cooking times. Times and temperatures can be altered safely as long as the food is thoroughly cooked. Always follow the recommendations at the beginning of this Chapter.

COOKING RED MEAT

The choice of methods for cooking red meat will depend on a number of factors most particularly the cut. Particular cuts of meat are better suited to particular cooking methods. Different cuts of meat have varying amounts of connective tissue present. Cheaper cuts of meat generally have more connective tissue and should be cooked slowly at low temperatures for a long time by a moist heating method, and so convert the connective tissue into gelatine. Cuts from older animals or parts of the body which do more work, such as the neck, will have more connective tissue. Cuts from younger beasts or muscle that is not used to any great extent will have less connective tissue and smaller muscle fibres. These are more suitable for speedy cooking, eg. grilling, frying etc. Prolonged cooking will result in stringy, dry meat.

Roasting

Pre-heat the oven at 180 degrees Celsius/350 degrees Fahrenheit, Gas Mark 4 and calculate the cooking time according to the weight.

Beef	25 minutes per 450g (1lb) plus 25 minutes
Lamb	30 minutes per 450g (1lb) plus 30 minutes
Pork	35 minutes per 450g (1lb) plus 35 minutes

If foil or roasting bags are used the cooking times may need to be increased slightly. During roasting the natural fats in the meat baste the joint. If the joint is a lean cut, the juices from the meat can be poured over the meat occasionally to prevent drying out. Meat shrinks during cooking because the connective tissue contracts. This process will bring juices - a mixture of fat and water - to the surface. Meat naturally contains 75% water.

Grilling

Grilling times vary according to the thickness of the meat. Thin portions can be cooked on a higher heat for a shorter time, thick portions require a moderate to low heat for a longer period.
Pre-heat the grill and cook as follows:

Rare beef steak	2.5 minutes each side
Well done beef steak	6 minutes each side
Minute steak	1 minute each side
Fillet steak	5 minutes each side
Lamb chops	5-8 minutes each side
Lamb cutlets	3-5 minutes each side
Pork chops	8-10 minutes each side
Sausages	10-12 minutes turning constantly
Liver and Kidney	10-12 minutes turning constantly

The above recommendations are for meat 2-3 cm thick, except for the minute steak which is as thin as possible. If your meat is thicker than this then increase the cooking time accordingly.

Frying

Cook the meat for two minutes on a high heat which will seal in the juices. Reduce the heat and turn the meat frequently.

Beef steak	(1/2 cm thick) 1-2 minutes
Beef steak	(2 cm thick) 7-10 minutes
Lamb chops	10-15 minutes
Lamb cutlets	8-10 minutes
Pork	10-15 minutes
Sausages	20 minutes

Try to use the bare minimum of oil.

Casseroling

Red meat can be casseroled with vegetables and seasoning. This form of cooking is especially good for cheaper cuts of meat. Cook in a moderate to low oven at 180 degrees Celsius, 350 degrees Fahrenheit or Gas Mark 4 for 1.5 hours to 2 hours. (If cooking large quantities, extend the cooking time). Some casserole recipes require the meat to be browned by fast frying before being gently casseroled.

Microwaving

	Cooking time guidelines for 450g (1lb) full power	Total standing time (covered/wrapped in foil)
Beef steak	Rare: 4-5 minutes Medium: 7 minutes Well done: 9 minutes	2 minutes
Minced Beef	5 minutes	2 minutes
Beef joint	Rare: 4-5 minutes Medium: 7 minutes Well done: 9 minutes	20 minutes
Lamb/Pork cutlets/chops	7-9 minutes	2 minutes
Lamb/Pork joints	7-9 minutes	25 minutes
Bacon rashers	6 minutes approximately 1 minute per rasher	2 minutes

Microwave oven cooking times in this book are calculated on a 650W oven. Conversions are required for lower or higher power ovens (see page III-6).

Use an appropriate (non-metal) trivet or grill that lifts the meat off the plate - this allows the juices to drip from the meat and will improve the efficiency of the microwave oven. Place meat in an appropriate roasting bag which will help the browning process. Alternatively use a browning dish. (NB. Do not use a metal tie, string is preferable). Turn joints over half way through cooking, or move the position of portions on a plate, or stir, in the case of mince. Stirring or turning food will reduce the likelihood of cold spots. Cover bacon during cooking with a piece of white kitchen towel or greaseproof paper as it tends to splatter.

Observe standing times which will allow heat transfer from hot to cooler areas. If you remove meat from the microwave oven it may still be cooking. Keep the food covered while it is standing. If you do not have a bowl large enough, use aluminium foil. Do not cover hot food with cling film.

COOKING POULTRY

Roasting

Pre-heat the oven to 190 degrees Celsius/375 degrees Fahrenheit, Gas Mark 5, and calculate the cooking time of the bird by its weight. Allow 20 minutes per 450g (1lb) plus 20 minutes extra. If the bird is stuffed include the weight of the stuffing in the calculation. Never fully stuff a large bird as this will lead to poor heat transfer and it will not cook properly. Only stuff the neck end of a bird loosely and do not stuff the tail end. If you are concerned about the bird drying out, add some fruit or onion to the cavity and cook any excess stuffing separately. If you wrap the bird in foil, increase the cooking time by a little - large birds should not be wrapped in foil.

To test if the bird is cooked insert a skewer into the thickest part of the leg. If the juices run clear it is ready. If they are still pink, return the bird to the oven for a further 15-20 minutes. Alternatively, test by gripping the drum stick and moving it. It should wobble freely, and not feel rigid and stiff. Allow the bird to stand for 15 minutes before carving.

Grilling

Grilling is only suitable for thin portions such as drumsticks or breast portions. A moderately hot grill should be used. Cook for 20-30 minutes turning frequently. The meat should change from a translucent to an opaque state. If this has not happened, cook for a further 5-10 minutes.

Casseroling

Poultry can be casseroled whole or in portions. Cook in a moderate oven 190 degrees Celsius/ 375 degrees Fahrenheit, Gas Mark 5 for approximately 1.5 hours to 2 hours depending on the size of the bird if cooking whole. The poultry should be placed in an oven-proof dish and covered with stock, herbs and seasoning. If you want to use less liquid, 1-2 cm in the bottom of the container should suffice. Place the lid on the container and cook as above. Once the bird is cooked, the meat should be tender and fall away from the bone.

Boiling

Put the poultry joints into a saucepan. Seasoning and vegetables should be added if required. Add enough stock or water to cover and bring the water to the boil. Once the liquid is boiling, remove the excess fat and continue to simmer gently for 20-25 minutes per 450g (1lb). If you are boiling a whole bird the cooking time should be increased to 45 minutes per 450g (1lb).

Frying

Poultry can be fried both in deep and shallow fat. Minced or diced poultry can be stir fried easily and quickly. Fast fry and stop when the meat is opaque or feels firm. Drain well.

Microwaving

We would not recommend or support microwave oven guidelines for raw poultry due to the difficulties in ensuring minimum temperatures are reached near the bone.

COOKING FISH

Fish is a very delicate food. If mishandled when cooking it can easily lose its texture and flavour. A fresh well-gutted fish only requires light cooking. If fish is overcooked it has a tendency to be dry and tough.

Baking

Fish cooked in the oven is referred to as baked rather than roasted. This method is suitable for small whole fish, fillets or steaks. For small fish, fillets or steaks heat the oven to 200 degrees Celsius/400 degrees Fahrenheit Gas Mark 6, and bake for 15-20 minutes depending on the size of the fish. To prevent drying out, wrap the fish in a foil parcel or baste regularly. Additional flavour may be added by cooking with herbs or vegetables or basting with a little wine or seasoned stock. If cooking a particularly large whole fish, cook in a preheated oven at 180 degrees Celsius/ 350 degrees Fahrenheit Gas Mark 4 allowing approximately 15 minutes per 450g (1lb).

Grilling

Grilling is a fast, effective way of cooking fish. It is suitable for small whole fish, steaks and fillets. Pre-heat the grill and line the grill pan with aluminium foil. Coat with a little oil to prevent the fish sticking. Add seasoning if required. A light brushing of oil will help retain moisture. Cook for 8-10 minutes then remove from the heat immediately. If you are grilling a whole fish make deep diagonal slashes through the skin and flesh to allow fast penetration of heat.

Poaching and Steaming

Steaming is an ideal method of cooking all fish especially fillets or flat fish.

Pre-heat the water in the base of the steamer to simmering point. Place the fish in the steamer and cover with the lid. Fillets or pieces of fish can be wrapped in aluminium foil and seasoned with herbs or vegetables.

Steaming should take about 10-15 minutes. It is important not to let the water boil fast or dry up. If cooking a large fish, the cooking time needs to be extended taking care not to overcook the fish. Poaching is rather like steaming except the fish comes into direct contact with the liquid in which it is cooked.

Warm the poaching liquid in the pan. Suitable liquids include fish or chicken stock, milk, wine, cider or water. Add seasoning and poach for 5-8 minutes in an uncovered pan remembering never to let the liquid boil.

Remove the fish and place on a serving plate. The liquid often makes a good base for an accompanying sauce.

Frying

Frying is a very quick cooking method. Shallow frying or stir frying is most suitable for fish fillets, steaks or small seafood. If the fish is coated with seasoned flour or egg and breadcrumbs, the coating will provide a crisp pleasant texture, and help prevent the fish breaking up. Pre-heat the oil. Shallow frying will take 3-10 minutes depending on the thickness of the fish, or pieces of fish. If you are frying larger fillets or whole fish, start on a high heat to seal the coating then turn the heat down and cook slowly until the fish is tender.

Deep frying is a popular and traditional method of cooking fish. The fish should always be coated with batter, flour or egg and breadcrumbs, to prevent it from breaking up. The fat or oil chosen for cooking is important so as not to mask the flavour of the fish. Pre-heat the oil to between 170 degrees Celsius/340 degrees Fahrenheit, to 190 degrees Celsius /375 degrees Fahrenheit.

The temperature will depend on the thickness of the fish. Test the oil temperature with a small cube of bread. The bread should sizzle briskly but not too furiously, and should brown in one minute. Cooking should take 3-4 minutes and the fish should then be drained well before serving. Change the cooking oil often and do not top it up.

Microwaving

Microwave oven cooking times for fish must take account of the size, shape and type of fish.

	Cooking time guidelines for 450g (1lb) full power	**Total standing time** (covered/wrapped in foil)
Cod/Haddock fillets/steaks	4 minutes	4-8 minutes
Plaice/Sole filleted	3 minutes	4-8 minutes
Trout (gutted but whole)	4 minutes each side	4-5 minutes
Kippers	4-5 minutes	4-5 minutes

Microwave oven cooking times in this book are calculated for a 650W oven. Conversions are required for lower or higher power ovens (see page III-6).

Fish should be arranged so that the thinnest part is towards the centre of the dish and the thickest on the edge. It should always be cooked in a single layer and not stacked. Make two small nicks in the skin of a large fish so that steam can escape. Parts of the fish that may overcook such as the tail or fins can be covered with small pieces of aluminium foil. (See page III-8 for information about metal in microwave ovens). Cover the container with a lid, plate or greaseproof paper in order to keep the fish moist. A microwave-safe cling film may be used to cover a container but remember to pierce it to allow air to escape. Do not wrap the fish directly in cling film. Additional liquid is not always necessary as the fish will cook in its own juices.

PRESSURE COOKING

Q: What is a pressure cooker? How does it work?

A: The boiling point of pure water is 100 degrees Celsius. The addition of salt raises the temperature at which boiling point is reached, which means the food in the water will be cooked quicker. Altering the pressure will also raise the boiling point of water. At high pressures, the boiling point of water will increase and food will cook quicker as more heat is transferred from the water to the food in a shorter period.

It is important to follow the pressure cooker manufacturer's instructions. Cooking times will vary for different foods and will also depend on the size of the food pieces being cooked. Provided that enough time is allowed for the heat to reach the centre of the solid particles in the food this form of cooking is safe. The temperatures achieved in a pressure cooker are capable of killing any bacteria present.

Q: Do they blow up?

A: No. Provided that the pressure cooker is well maintained.
It is very important to check safety gauges and vents on your pressure cooker. If you are using a very old pressure cooker, make sure it is functioning properly by seeking professional advice. The rubber vent should not have perished and must be capable of withstanding high pressures but must also allow excess pressure to escape. If you are in doubt, contact the manufacturer. Do not leave a pressure cooker on a high heat unattended. If you are in the kitchen the cooker will warn you that it is too hot by hissing and letting off short bursts of steam. The lid will not blow off but you should reduce the heat.

SLOW COOKING

Q: What is a slow cooker?

A: A slow cooker is exactly that. It stews very slowly bringing out the flavour of casseroles and making the meat tender but not stringy. It is also suitable for vegetable dishes and soups.

Q: What is the difference between a high and low setting on a slow cooker?

A: Both the high and the low settings on a slow cooker ultimately reach the same temperature of 92 degrees Celsius. The difference between the two settings is the speed at which the temperature is achieved. The high setting reaches the temperature within 30 minutes, the low setting however takes longer. The longer, slower cooking is preferable for tougher cuts of meat like stewing steak.

Q: Are slow cookers safe?

A: Yes. Provided that the cooker is functioning correctly and is reaching the right temperature.

Q: Can I cook chille-con-carne with red kidney beans?

A: Yes, but boil the dried beans first as directed on page I-20. 92 degrees Celsius is not hot enough to render the beans harmless.

Q: Is there anything I should be careful about?

A: If stewing meat or chicken in the slow cooker, turn it on as soon as you load it. Don't let the warm contents stand in a warm kitchen for hours before cooking. If you prepare the stew in advance, keep refrigerated until you cook it. Either keep food hot ie. keep the cooker on or cool food and refrigerate it. Never turn the cooker off and leave the contents in the cooker after cooking. Take care when reheating. Do not keep adding to the stew in order to top it up. You can only reheat food once (see page II-6).

MICROWAVES

Q: Are microwave ovens safe?

A: Yes. However microwave ovens, like any other form of electrical appliance or cooking implement, should be treated with care. If correctly used, a microwave oven is as safe as any kitchen appliance. Remember, at certain times the voltage of the mains power supply may be reduced, and successive use of microwave ovens may reduce the power output. Therefore longer cooking times may well be needed. Consumer experience however, has a role to play as with other forms of cooking.

Q: Can microwaves escape and get into the air?

A: Microwaves are naturally present in the air. They come from the sun, stars and are found at high levels during thunderstorms. Microwaves are a form of electro magnetic energy similar to radio waves and X-rays, only much smaller. Microwave energy at the level used domestically does not penetrate metal but is merely reflected back. A microwave oven is an enclosed metal box. The microwave oven door is often made of reinforced glass with a special metal screen and any ventilation grills will be shielded by metal. The microwaves generated by the electricity will be reflected around the oven until they are absorbed by something non-metal such as food.

Your microwave oven should be serviced regularly and a check of the door seal included.

Q: How do microwaves heat food?

A: Microwave energy is absorbed by the molecules (particles that make up all matter) in the food which are excited, releasing energy in the form of heat. Microwaves are an efficient way of heating food, especially those containing a lot of water such as vegetables.

Q: Can you cook fatty food in a microwave oven?

A: Yes. However fatty foods do heat up very quickly in microwave ovens and therefore care must be taken.

DO NOT LEAVE THE MICROWAVE OVEN UNATTENDED WHEN IN OPERATION

Q: Can microwaves kill Listeria and Salmonella?

A: Microwaves will not, by themselves, kill any bacteria. Microwave ovens do how-ever, heat up the food and it is the heat that will kill any **Listeria** and **Salmonella** present. It is important to ensure that the correct cooking temperatures are achieved, as with any other form of cooking.

We would recommend that food reaches and is maintained at 70 degrees Celsius for two minutes. This temperature will ensure that any bacteria present and capable of causing gastroenteritis will be killed.

Q: Can bacteria survive in cold spots? If so, how can cold spots be prevented?

A: Yes. If cold spots are present in food - areas where the food has not reached a temperature of at least 70 degrees Celsius for a minimum of two minutes - potentially harmful bacteria can survive. It is therefore important to change the position of the food in the microwave oven to prevent cold spots from occurring. It is also important to stir food or observe standing times so that the food can reach an even temperature. Standing times for food vary. If there are no manufacturer guidelines these recommendations may be applied:

▷ Stand small items and reheated food for a couple of minutes.
▷ Stir liquid items for example, soups and stews; and then stand for a couple of minutes.
▷ Large or dense items that cannot be stirred should stand for longer. For example, a family size lasagne should stand for about ten minutes (a recommended standing time is given for joints in the preceding sections of this book. Page II-9).

Food should always be reheated until it is piping hot. It is better to slightly overheat food and allow it to cool a little than to underheat it.

If your microwave oven is functioning correctly you should not have to extend the manufacturer's recommended cooking times. If in doubt, check the temperature of the food with a food thermometer. If food is not thoroughly cooked or reheated, bacteria will survive. Your microwave oven should be serviced regularly. If in any doubt about the performance of the microwave oven and its ability to heat food properly, contact the microwave oven manufacturer.

Q: What is the best way to test the temperature of food cooking in a microwave oven?

A: Microwave oven thermometer probes are available from nearly all shops selling ovens. (Do not use glass thermometers to check temperature of food).

If the food is of uneven thickness the temperature should be tested in the centre of the thickest part. If it is of uniform thickness take the temperature in two or three places to make sure the correct heat has been reached throughout. Keep the thermometer clean; putting a dirty thermometer into food can add bacteria to it.

Q: What are the new microwave oven labels?

A: The new microwave oven labels are part of a voluntary labelling scheme for ovens and food packs. The scheme has been developed by the Ministry of Agriculture, Fisheries and Food (MAFF) together with consumer organisations, oven manufacturers, food manufacturers and retailers.

Q: Why do we need new microwave oven labels?

A: There are two main reasons:
▷ Research organisations have shown that different microwave ovens have varying abilities to reheat small packets of food such as ready meals. This would not automatically be obvious to the consumer and so an alpha graded heating category system has been developed. By following this system you may achieve 'Standard cook' to produce a more consistent product.
▷ A new international standard (IEC) test method has been developed which can be used to calculate the power output of the oven. This IEC method replaces the old British Standard (BS) test system which was not adaptable. The IEC power output enables easier identification of oven power output which varies considerably across different makes.

Q: What information do the new microwave oven labels give us?

A: The heating category is an indication of how quickly the microwave oven can heat small quantities of food. The power output (wattage) is a guide to how quickly the microwave oven can heat large quantities of food.

Q: Is it really necessary to have both these systems?

A: Yes. The amount of energy delivered into food cooking in a microwave oven depends partly on the amount of food being heated in the oven cavity.
The food may not be able to absorb all the energy available if the quantity of food is small. This does not mean that the oven design is faulty, it is just a reflection of complicated physics involved. By following the heating category

guidelines corresponding to your oven when heating small quantities of food, you are following the best match for the best performance.

Q: What do the new labels look like?

A: Ovens that are tested using the new system will be labelled like the example below.

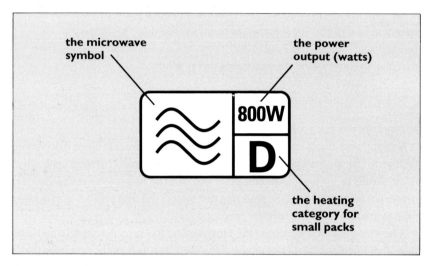

Q: How can I find out what the IEC 705 power output of my microwave oven is?

A: Use any of the following methods:

1. Check the model number and make against the list of power outputs declared in the MAFF leaflet 'The New Microwave Labels'.
2. Contact the manufacturer or the retailer from whom you bought your microwave oven.
3. Buy a microwave oven home test kit from a microwave oven dealer, leading supermarket or major kitchenware shop.

Q: What if the old declared wattage is different from the new IEC 705 power rating?

A: Make a note of the new rating, this can be regarded as the true wattage of your oven.

Q: If you know the power output, why do you need to know the heating category?

A: Knowing the heating category for your microwave oven, will help you calculate more precisely the time it takes to cook small items of food, such as individual portions or microwave meals.

Ovens are assigned a heating category letter from A to E. Category E denotes the largest power output to a small load, Category A the smallest. The smaller the power output the longer the food will need to be heated to attain the required temperature.

Q: How do you know what the heating category for an oven is?

A: 1. Refer to the list in the MAFF publication 'The New Microwave Labels'.
2. Contact the manufacturer or retailer who sold you the oven, quoting the oven make and model number.
3. Purchase a microwave oven home test kit from a microwave oven dealer, leading supermarket or major kitchenware shop.

Once you know the heating category of your microwave oven, you should follow the corresponding guidelines relevant to that heating category given on the microwave meal. If you do not know the heating category, you can still cook the food in your microwave oven but you will have to follow the guidelines for the known power output. Remember to check that the food is piping hot before serving.

Q: Why not just follow the guidelines for the IEC 705 power output (watts) anyway?

A: By following the heating category guidelines you are following the 'best fit' guidelines for small packs. The heating category indicates how efficient a microwave oven is. For example, consider two microwave oven models with an IEC power output of 650W, one with a heating category D, the other with a heating category B. Both these ovens would perform in a similar manner if used to cook a large meal such as a family casserole. However, when heating small portions (such as microwave meals) the one with heating category B would take longer to cook the food

If you follow the guidelines for power output (ie the IEC 705 wattage rating) you may end up slightly over heating or slightly under heating the meal. This is why it is important to always check that food is piping hot throughout before serving.

Q: When do you use the small food pack guidelines and when do you use the power output (watts)?

A: Small food pack (heating category) guidelines are useful for cooking anything weighing up to 500g - typically ready meals for 1 - 2 people. Anything weighing more than 500g should be cooked using the guidelines for the power output.

Heating Category	
B	D
8 mins	6 mins

Q: How do you follow the heating category guidelines?

Here is a worked example:
A: In the example, information is given for ovens in categories B and D. For the example given:
▷ For A category ovens it is necessary to heat the food for a longer time than given for B (as A ovens are slower) - cook for 9 minutes.
▷ For B ovens cook for 8 minutes.
▷ For C ovens choose the time that is midway between the B and D categories - cook for 7 minutes.
▷ For D ovens cook for 6 minutes.
▷ For E ovens use a shorter time than for D ovens (as E ovens are faster) - cook for 5 minutes.
Always check the food is piping hot after heating.

Oven Wattage	
650W	750W
7 mins	5 mins

Q: How do you use oven wattage guidelines?

A: If you do not yet know the heating category for your oven you can follow the guidelines for the known oven wattage. For the example given:
▷ Ovens with a power output of less than 650W will require a longer time to cook the food. For example, a 550W oven will require approximately 9 minutes to cook the food.
▷ Ovens with a power output of 650W will require a cooking time of approximately 7 minutes.
▷ Ovens with a power output of 700W require a cooking time mid-way between that for a 650W oven and a 750W oven - approximately 6 minutes.

▷ Ovens with a power output of 750W require a cooking time of approximately 5 minutes.

▷ Ovens with a power output greater than 750W are faster and so cooking times should be reduced. In this example for an 850W oven, cook for approximately 4 - 4½ minutes.

Remember that the wattage guidelines are not instructions they are meant only as a guide. Once the food has finished cooking you should always check that it is piping hot throughout.

Q: Are standing times affected by the change in microwave oven labels?

A: No. Standing times remain the same. Standing times allow heat to be conducted from hot areas to cooler areas and so prevent cold spots.

Q: Will it still be necessary to stir and turn food?

A: Yes. Always check the guidelines given. Most foods heat more evenly if they are stirred and turned in order to prevent cold spots. Once food is cooked you should always check that it is piping hot throughout.

Q: How hot is piping hot?

A: Piping hot is when food reaches a temperature in excess of 70 degrees Celsius for over two minutes. To check this use a clean dry food thermometer or look for steam rising from every part of the food. If the food is not piping hot, return it to the oven and continue heating.

Q: What if I am cooking food from frozen?

A: Follow the guidelines on the pack. If these state defrost before cooking, you can use the defrost cycle on your microwave oven, but always ensure that the food is defrosted right the way through to the centre.

Always follow the guidelines given on the food pack.

Q: If the power output of my oven has changed, does this mean all my current recipes must change?

A: No. Remember your oven is still the same oven. Any recipes given in the manufacturer's handbook for your oven will remain the same. You have probably already adapted recipes for your individual oven. These recipes also remain the same.

Q: What about new recipes?

A: Any new recipes giving cooking guidelines for an oven with the same IEC 705 power rating as your oven can be adapted directly if you are cooking large quantities.

Similarly any new recipes giving cooking guidelines for an oven with the same heating category can be adapted directly if you are cooking small quantities of food. The recipes that will require alteration are those that you are adapting from an old recipe book or any that you have been given that are for an oven with a different rating. In such cases you should make sure that the guidelines given are capable of heating the food until it is piping hot.

Q: Is it safe to heat baby's milk in a microwave oven?

A: It is probably safer not to attempt to heat baby's milk in a microwave oven. Microwave ovens often tend to heat the contents faster than the container so it is always wise to test the temperature of food before attempting to eat it. Often the bottle may appear cold but the milk inside will be scalding hot. Sealed bottles or containers should never be heated in a microwave oven because the pressure of hot food (and expanding air) inside the container may cause it to explode, (this includes whole eggs in their shell).

Q: Is there any truth in the rumour that microwave ovens make proteins in food dangerous?

A: No. If food is cooked in an open container in a microwave oven, it will be perfectly safe. Food should not be cooked in sealed containers as this may lead to the food spoiling due to overheating, and to the container exploding.

Q: Is it dangerous to put metal in a microwave oven?

A: Putting a metal container in a microwave oven will not directly affect the wholesomeness of the food but over an extended period the microwave oven will be damaged. Metal in the microwave oven may cause flashing or sparking (called arcing) particularly if the metal comes into contact with the inside surface of the oven walls. Generally speaking the occasional flash will not damage the component parts of the microwave oven but it may lead to pitting in the oven walls.

Glass and china with decorative metal rims should not be placed in microwave ovens as this may lead to the decorative metal turning black. Use glass, ceramics or an approved plastic container instead.

Small pieces of foil used to protect delicate parts of food such as the tail of a fish will not affect the microwave oven, nor will shallow aluminium trays used inside a cardboard sleeve where this instruction is given on the food pack.

Q: How do I remove unpleasant smells from my microwave oven?

A: To remove unpleasant smells from your microwave oven, squeeze 2 tablespoons of lemon juice or vinegar into a bowl of water and microwave for 2-3 minutes. Then wipe down the surfaces with a clean damp cloth.

Q: Is it safe to put cling film in a microwave oven?

A: If you wish to use cling film in a microwave oven, check the instructions on the packet first, as some cling films are not suitable for use in a microwave oven. If suitable for microwave oven use, it may be used to cover bowls and containers or to cover food that is defrosting. It is important however to make sure that the film is not in direct contact with the food. Alternatively, use a vented microwave oven cover. Cling films should not be used to line dishes or directly wrap food that is being cooked in a microwave oven. For more information on cling film see Chapter XIII.

Q: Is it safe to heat liquids in a microwave oven?

A: Yes, but great care should be taken when heating liquids in a microwave oven. There have been reports of liquids in microwave ovens boiling over rapidly when the liquids are disturbed. The reason for this is not entirely clear. Such incidents have occurred with mugs of tea, coffee and hot milk, although thick liquids such as gravy or custard are also a concern.

Q: What steps can be taken to make heating liquids in a microwave oven safe?

A: The problem seems to occur when liquids are first disturbed after being heated in the microwave oven without interruption. There are several precautions that can be taken to prevent this:-
▷ Always stir the liquid during cooking and change the position of the container in the oven.
▷ Choose a container that has a good shape, a bowl shaped container with slopping sides is preferable to a container with parallel sides such as a mug or a tall jug.
▷ Always choose a container large enough for the quantity of food you wish to heat, the larger the better.

▷ Never fill a container more than 2/3 full.

▷ Cook thick liquids on a lower power setting remembering to stir frequently.

Microwave ovens often heat liquids more quickly than their container, so do not be fooled into thinking the liquid is cooler than it really is. Placing a microwave-safe plastic spoon or a thick heat-resistant glass rod, (available in some kitchenware shops) in the liquid will help to break up the surface tension of the liquid and may well prevent it from erupting.

Q: Is it safe to cook eggs in a microwave oven?

A: Cooking whole eggs whether poached, fried or boiled in a microwave oven can be dangerous because a great deal of pressure can build up inside the yolk membrane. The hot yolk could then explode when the egg is pierced. The Food Safety Advisory Centre would not recommend cooking whole eggs in a microwave oven. Scrambled eggs may be cooked provided they are stirred regularly during cooking and are piping hot right the way through to the centre before serving. Care should be taken to use a clean fork or spoon when stirring food in the microwave oven in order to prevent cross contamination.

Q: Is it safe to defrost in a microwave oven?

A: Yes. Microwave ovens are useful for defrosting food.

Q: What if food starts to heat up whilst defrosting in a microwave oven?

A: If food starts to heat up whilst defrosting, switch the microwave oven off and allow the food to stand for a short while. This will allow the heat to transfer from the hottest areas to the coldest. If the food remains hot it would be advisable to continue cooking as the warm, moist environment is an ideal place for bacteria to grow if present.

Q: Is it safe to reheat leftovers in a microwave oven?

A: Yes. Microwave ovens are useful for reheating food that has already been cooked. It is vitally important however to check that the food is piping hot before serving. It is not recommended to ever reheat food more than once.

FOOD PRESERVATION

FOOD PROCESSING

Raw food is not sterile. Bacteria are present in the environment and all food either contains bacteria or carries them on its surface. If the food is kept for long enough the bacteria may lead to food spoilage or pose a risk to health and cause illness.

The aim of food preservation is to destroy the bacteria or stop them growing and so lengthen the shelf life of the product and make it safer.

HEAT TREATMENT

One of the best examples of the use of heat treatment can be seen in the dairy industry. Here there are three heat treatment processes commonly used, pasteurisation, sterilisation and Ultra Heat Treatment (UHT).

PASTEURISATION

Pasteurised milk is the most familiar and pasteurisation, the most commonly used of these heat treatments in Britain. It involves the rapid heating of milk to 72 degrees Celsius; and this temperature is maintained for at least 15 seconds before the milk is rapidly cooled to less than 10 degrees Celsius. Pasteurisation destroys many of the bacteria present and results in a product that is low in micro-organisms.

Pasteurised milk is nutritionally close to raw milk, although the process does reduce the nutritional value slightly, (levels of Vitamin B12 and B1 are reduced by about 10% during pasteurisation).

STERILISATION

Sterilised milk has a longer shelf life than pasteurised milk because sterilisation, unlike pasteurisation, effectively destroys all the bacteria.

Sterilisation requires a more severe heat treatment. Bottles containing milk are heated to 104 degrees Celsius for 40 minutes or 113 degrees Celsius for 15 minutes. If unopened it will keep for several months or even years if the seal remains intact. Once opened sterilised milk has the same shelf life as pasteurised milk - about 4 to 5 days if refrigerated. The high temperatures used to sterilise milk mean that there is a more significant vitamin loss than in pasteurisation (approximately 30% of vitamin B1, and up to 50% of vitamin B12, will be destroyed). In addition there are some losses of lycine, a nutritionally required amino acid. The heat treatment also affects the flavour of the milk because the milk sugar (lactose) is caramelised. However, this will not affect its energy value significantly.

ULTRA HEAT TREATMENT (UHT)

UHT, which involves ultra high temperature treatment, will effectively destroy all bacteria but will leave the majority of the vitamins intact.

The milk is heated to between 132 degrees Celsius to 140 degrees Celsius for up to 5 seconds and then quickly cooled. This process effectively renders the milk sterile. The nutritional value of UHT milk is similar to pasteurised but the taste is like sterilised milk because of the caramelisation of the milk sugar (although caramelisation is less marked). After treatment, the milk is packed under sterile conditions and can keep for several months without requiring refrigeration. Once opened and exposed to the atmosphere UHT milk has the same shelf life as pasteurised milk - 4-5 days in the refrigerator.

CHEMICAL PRESERVATION

The use of chemicals in the preservation of food is not new. Traditional processes such as curing bacon or smoking fish have always been dependent on the chemicals applied during the processing, either to prevent bacteria growing or kill any bacteria present. Modern techniques rely on similar principles.

Q: What is curing?

A: Food processed in this way includes meat, sausages and meat products. Originally meat was preserved by salting without refrigeration. Most cured meats today have other ingredients added and are refrigerated; many are also smoked. Curing agents include sodium chloride (common salt), sugar, sodium nitrate, sodium nitrite and vinegar. Only the first four are commonly used in meat curing.

Different curing agents have the effect of adding flavour and fixing colour.

There are four methods of curing :

1. Dry Cure – The dry salts are rubbed into the meat.
2. Pickle Cure – Meats are immersed in a solution of the salts.
3. Injection Cure – A concentrated solution of the agents are injected by needle into the arteries and veins of the meat or into the muscular tissue.
4. Direct Addition – The curing agents are added directly to finely ground meats, such as sausage. The curing temperature is usually just above 2 degrees Celsius

and the time of cure varies with the methods and meats used. Many meats are smoked after curing to aid their preservation. However, corned beef, for example, is not smoked but is sterilised during the canning process and is refrigerated after opening. Salt discourages microbial growth.

Q: What is smoking?

A: Food processed by smoking include meats, fish, sausages and cheese. The smoking of foods usually has two main purposes: to add flavour and to aid preservation. It may also improve the colour of the inside of the meat and give a 'gloss' to the outside, making it more tender. The smoking process preserves food in a number of ways: by impregnating it near the surface with chemical preservatives from the smoke; by the combined action of heat and preservatives during smoking; and by the drying effect especially on the surface. Smoking is carried out by burning wood, corn cobs or other materials. Sawdust is added to the fire to give a heavy smudge (smoke). Temperature, humidity levels and smoking time depends on the type of food. Smoking temperatures for meats vary from 43-71 degrees Celsius and the smoking period from a few hours to several days.

Some smoked food is 'hot smoked' i.e. it cooks as it smokes (eg mackerel/ trout), other food is 'cold smoked' and so the food is essentially eaten raw (eg smoked salmon). Smoking prevents bacterial growth, however, it is less effective against moulds. Liquid smoke, a solution of chemicals similar to those found in wood smoke, has little or no preservative effect, though it contributes to flavour.

Q: Are food additives preservatives?

A: Not all food additives are preservatives. Some additives preserve food but others have different functions such as adding colour to food or thickening food. See Chapter VII.

TEMPERATURE CONTROL

Temperature control is a very effective way of extending the shelf life of food, as micro-organisms reproduce rapidly at room temperature. They can double in number every hour if given suitable conditions.

Reducing the temperature at which food is stored, by placing it in a refrigerator or freezer, slows the growth of micro-organisms present in the food and so slows spoilage. If the temperature is reduced sufficiently, micro-organisms will stop reproducing completely. The temperature at which growth stops will depend on the bacterium under consideration. Once the temperature of the food has been reduced to 0 degrees Celsius pathogenic bacteria will cease to grow. Lowering the temperature will also slow down any chemical reactions that are taking place in the food. We have all seen chemical reactions take place, for example, when you cut an apple in half, the flesh turns brown. Chemical reactions usually affect the quality of food but do not normally affect its safety.

Q: How does a 'fridge work?

A: A refrigerator is an insulated cabinet with a cooling mechanism designed to maintain a cool temperature which will keep stored food fresh for longer than if stored in ambient. The cooling mechanism involves a fluid called refrigerant, which by compression and expansion, is changed from liquid to gas and back to liquid, in a continuous cycle. This is usually driven by an electric motor. Heat is extracted from the storage compartment of the refrigerator as a result of this continuous cycle of liquid refrigerant evaporating to a gas.

When siting your 'fridge take care not to locate it next to a boiler, a radiator, an oven, a tumble drier, in a tight corner, or in constant sunlight, as these areas may be too warm. Also check that a garage or outhouse is not too damp or too cold. Any extremes of temperature will affect the performance of the refrigerator.

Make sure your refrigerator is in good working order and defrost regularly. If you need to defrost very frequently, check the door seals are not damaged. Check the age of your 'fridge - eight to nine years is the average useful life of a 'fridge.

Q: At what temperature should my refrigerator operate?

A: The dial inside the 'fridge controls the thermostat which keeps the internal temperature constant. Your refrigerator should be adjusted to the coldest setting which does not cause the contents to freeze. This should be less than 5 degrees Celsius (41°F)

The actual temperature range of any 'fridge depends on the siting of the refrigerator coil. The bottom of the 'fridge is the coldest part (cold air falls). The top shelf will be the warmest.

Q: What is the maximum time I should keep various foods in the 'fridge?

A: Assuming the food is in good condition when put in the 'fridge, that it is correctly protected and that the 'fridge temperature is correct, we recommend the following maximum storage times. The storage times are intended as a rough guide only. It is important to also follow package instructions. For perishable food follow the 'use by' date or in the absence of such a date follow the suggested list overleaf.

MAXIMUM REFRIGERATOR STORAGE TIMES

Raw meats

Joints	3 days
Poultry	2 days
Raw Sliced Meat	2 days
Minced meat	1 day
Liver, Kidney, etc.	1 day
Sausages	3 days
Bacon	7 days
Vacuum packed bacon	2 - 3 weeks
Raw Fish	1 day
Raw Kippers	1 day
Smoked Salmon	2 days

Cooked meats

Joints	3 days
Casseroles	2 days
Sliced meat	2 days
Ham	2 days
Pies	2 days
Cooked Fish	1 day

Dairy foods

Milk (pasteurised, homogenised)	4 - 5 days
Cheese, soft	2 - 3 days
Cheese, hard	7 - 14 days
Cheese, semi-hard	7 - 10 days
Eggs (raw)*	2 weeks
Eggs (hard boiled)◤	2 days

Desserts

Fruit Pies	2 days
Custard	1 day
Rice Pudding	1 day

Drinks

Freshly Squeezed Fruit Juice	1 day

Leftover foods

Cooked Vegetables	2 days
Cooked Potatoes	2 days
Cooked Rice △	1 day
Canned Food ⊙	2 days

* All raw eggs should be stored in a 'fridge.

◤ Once cooked hard boiled eggs should not be returned to their original container. If you wish to store hard boiled eggs, do so in a clean dry bowl with a lid.

△ Cooked rice should be cooled quickly, transferred to a clean dry container within 1 hour of cooking and stored in the 'fridge. Storage should be for no more than 1 day and the rice must be thoroughly reheated before eating.

⊙ Canned food once opened should be transferred to a clean dry container with a lid.

Remember, do not place hot food directly into a refrigerator. The excess heat will affect the refrigerator temperature and warm other food stored in the 'fridge. It is important to also check the best before/use by date of the product to make sure it is not being exceeded and any other storage instructions where applicable.

Q: How can I cool food quickly?

A: Cool food before placing it in the 'fridge by transferring the food into a suitable clean, dry container. Small quantities will cool quite quickly, larger quantities should be either divided into smaller portions, or transferred to a container with a large surface area. If available, place on a cooling rack to allow air to circulate.

Whilst cooling the food do not cover; the steam should be allowed to evaporate. If the food is susceptible to insect or fly contamination cover with a clean, dry muslin cloth.

During excessively warm weather conditions, or if handling large quantities, place the container in cold water, changing the water frequently to speed the cooling time. Ensure the food is cooled within a maximum of 1 hour, then cover the dish before placing in the refrigerator.

Q: If I buy frozen food, how long can I keep it in the 'fridge/freezer?

A: Always check on the packet as instructions may vary from food to food. As a general guide :

Main Compartment of 'Fridge or other cool place +5 degrees Celsius or less than	Eat within 24 hours of purchase.
One star marked Frozen Food Compartment Temperature -6 degrees Celsius	Eat within 1 week of purchase.
Two star marked Frozen Food Compartment Temperature -12 degrees Celsius	Eat within 1 month of purchase.
Three star marked Frozen Food Compartment Temperature -18 degrees Celsius	Eat within 3 months of purchase.
Food Freezer Temperature -18 degrees Celsius	Eat within 3 months of purchase.

REMEMBER DO NOT RE-FREEZE FOOD ONCE THAWED

A CHECKLIST FOR THE USE OF REFRIGERATORS

1. Take care to arrange foods in a 'fridge to avoid cross-contamination i.e. the transfer of micro-organisms from, for example, raw foods to cooked foods, vegetables to other foods.

2. Store raw meat and poultry separately from other foods, below cooked foods and dairy products, so as to avoid dripping onto foods below.

3. Always keep foods covered.

4. Always cool food before placing in the 'fridge. (see How can I cool food quickly?).

5. Do not overfill the 'fridge, make sure there is adequate air circulation.

6. Keep the 'fridge door open for as short a time as possible and ensure the door seals are in good condition.

7. Where appropriate, defrost frozen food in the 'fridge but make sure that it does not drip onto other foods.

8. Take care not to keep food for too long. Follow the manufacturers instructions including use by/best before dates. If you are in any doubt, throw it away.

9. Get shopping home as quickly as possible, ideally using a cool bag for chilled and frozen foods. Once home put chilled and frozen food into the refrigerator or freezer. Delay in putting these foods into the refrigerator will allow the temperature to rise. It is especially important not to leave them out at a warm temperature for hours as can all too easily happen in an office or when travelling.

10. Make sure your refrigerator is working properly and defrost regularly. After defrosting clean and dry thoroughly.

11. Adjust your refrigerator control to the coldest setting, which does not cause the contents to freeze.

12. Check that drips from uncooked food have not contaminated the salad tray.

13. When handling foods it is important that your hands are clean. Wash hands after handling raw food, before handling cooked foods.

14. Always keep your 'fridge and freezer clean. Always mop up spilled foods and drinks, and clean out salad drawers and freezer compartments.

15. During heatwaves food often goes off much more rapidly, this is because the micro-organisms flourish under warm conditions. One precaution you can take is to make a temporary extra 'fridge by using a freezer box or polystyrene box and placing a frozen container of liquid or freezer bottles in it. This container will be suitable for keeping items like milk cool or preventing butter from going rancid.

DIAGRAM OF 'FRIDGE

1. Fruit, vegetables, salad items should be stored in the salad drawer.

2. Milk, fruit juices should be stored in the bottle rack in the door. This will, however, depend on the design of your 'fridge.

3. Butter, lard, margarines, cheese, preserves, salad dressings, spreads, sauces, eggs, should be stored on the centre or top shelves.

4. Fresh meat, cooked meat, ham, sausages, milk products, cream, fish, should be stored above the salad drawer. NB. package meats separately. Store raw meat and poultry below cooked meats and dairy products.

5. Convenience foods and cooked items should be stored on top and centre shelves.

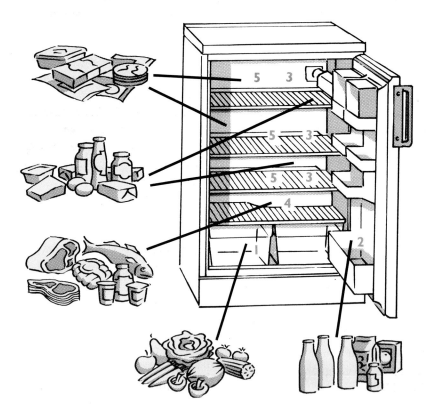

FREEZING

Most micro-organisms cease to multiply at cold refrigerator temperatures (5 degrees Celsius). Some can still multiply when refrigerated but will cease growing at frozen food temperatures. Food spoilage is reduced as temperatures fall below freezing and at -8 degrees Celsius (17 degrees Fahrenheit) bacteria and moulds stop developing. At these low temperatures the physical and chemical changes in food take place more slowly but do not stop completely, therefore frozen food cannot be kept indefinitely. Storing frozen food for too long affects its quality in different ways, for example, fat will eventually oxidise and go rancid. Certain foods are more likely than others to undergo quality deterioration. Try to use frozen food in rotation and follow the recommended storage times given in this chapter.

Q: How does a freezer work?

A: A freezer works on the same principle as a 'fridge, but the refrigerant is at a higher pressure and the evaporator and heat exchanger are bigger, making it possible to achieve very low temperatures.

Q: What is the maximum time I should keep various foods in the freezer?

A: Food poisoning bacteria cannot grow in products stored at the correct temperature in properly working domestic freezers. However, the food's colour and quality will slowly deteriorate. For pre-packaged goods follow the package instructions. If none are given, or the product is frozen by yourself, we recommend the following times for a four-star freezer. Remember that the packaging should be intact to avoid dehydration and excessive flavour loss.

Meat and Poultry

Beef and Lamb	4-6 months
Pork and Veal	4-6 months
Offal	3-4 months
Ham and Bacon joints	3-4 months
Chicken and Turkey	10-12 months
Duck and Goose	4-6 months
Venison	10-12 months
Rabbit and Hare	4-6 months
Sausages and Sausagemeat	2-3 months
Minced Beef	3-4 months

Fish

White Fish	6-8 months
Oily Fish	3-4 months
Fish Portions	3-4 months
Shellfish	2-3 months

Fruit and Vegetables

Fruit either with or without sugar	8-10 months
Fruit Juices	4-6 months
Most Vegetables	10-12 months
Mushrooms and Tomatoes	6-8 months
Vegetable Purees	6-8 months

Dairy produce

Cream	6-8 months
Butter - unsalted	6-8 months
Butter - salted	3-4 months
Cheese - hard	4-6 months
Cheese - soft	3-4 months
Ice Cream and similar products	3-4 months

Prepared foods

Ready prepared meals highly seasoned	2-3 months
Ready prepared meals - average seasoning	4-6 months
Boil-in-bag meals	4-6 months
Cakes	4-6 months
Bread - all kinds	2-3 months
Sandwiches	2-3 months
Bread Dough	2-3 months
Other yeast products/pastries	3-4 months
Canned Food *	2-3 months

* Canned food should be transferred to a tight fitting clean dry container with a lid. Unopened canned foods must never be stored in a domestic freezer.

A CHECKLIST FOR THE USE OF FREEZERS

1. Keep the freezer as full as possible, if necessary add bread. Empty spaces are costly in terms of energy consumption.

2. Make sure that food is clearly labelled and dated so that food can be easily identified and used within the recommended time (See: What is the maximum time I should keep various foods in the freezer?)

3. Store raw and cooked foods separately, with raw food below any cooked or ready-to-eat food.

4. Keep a record of the freezer contents and be sure to use older food first and so prevent wastage through prolonged storage.

5. It is important that food is not stored above the load line of the freezer (usually only applicable to chest freezers).

6. Do not place liquid filled bottles or sealed fizzy drink's cans in the freezer as they may burst.

7. If there is a power cut, keep the lid or door of the freezer closed and insulate with a blanket.

8. Try to defrost the freezer when stocks are low. While defrosting keep any remaining stocks as cold as possible - wrapped in newspaper or in a cold box.

9. If the warning light comes on indicating a rise in temperature, contact the service agent immediately and keep the lid or door closed until the engineer's arrival.

DEFROSTING FROZEN FOOD

It is difficult to give hard and fast rules for defrosting frozen food, however, as a guide follow the basic principles set out below.

Frozen food itself is not unsafe. Ice cream can be eaten from frozen as can hygienically prepared desserts such as cakes and washed fruit e.g strawberries. However, frozen raw uncooked food is potentially unsafe because although micro-organisms cannot multiply in the freezer, they can survive. Always allow large joints of meat or bulk items to defrost thoroughly before cooking.

HOW TO DEFROST

Defrost items on a tray or plate that is sufficiently deep to collect any liquid that drips from the thawed product. Avoid overloading the dish with several frozen items as this prolongs the thawing time and leads to the food on the outside of the dish thawing first.

Keep the food covered to prevent contamination from the atmosphere. Always thaw in a cool place, because although it takes longer, the food will thaw more thoroughly, and will be safer. For example, it is dangerous to thaw a large Christmas turkey in a warm kitchen. **Salmonella** may start to multiply on the warm surface of the bird while the inside is still frozen. It may also be misleading, as you may assume that if the outside is thawed that the inside of the bird is too. This may result in undercooking the bird as a sufficiently high heat will not penetrate it. If you are thawing in a microwave oven, observe the manufacturer's recommended standing times and check the items regularly. If ice crystals are still present continue thawing. If the items start warming, stand for a while to allow the heat to disperse. If the food remains warm, cook immediately. Warm food is the perfect incubator for bacteria.

Thawing times will depend on the thickness and weight of the food and we suggest you follow the guidelines given opposite.

You must remember to check the food before cooking. If large items still appear to be frozen give them more time to defrost, do not attempt to start cooking them. Smaller items of food may be cooked straight from frozen, like frozen vegetables, fish fillets or beef burgers. These items defrost quickly during the initial cooking stages. Bigger items of food should not be cooked from frozen. If in doubt, defrost before cooking. Use the defrost setting on the microwave oven. Do not defrost large items on High as the outside will cook before the centre thaws.

Always keep a check on items, do not blindly follow times stated below as these are guidelines only.

GUIDE TO THAWING TIMES

	Thawing in a Refrigerator	Thawing at a cool room Temperature	Thawing in a Microwave
Meat			
Joints over 1.5 Kg (3.3lb)	6-7 hours per 450g	2-3 hours per 450g	9-12 mins per 450g
Joints under 1.5 Kg (3.3lb)	3-4 hours per 450g	1-2 hours per 450g	9-12 mins per 450g
Steak or Chops 25cm (1 inch) thick	5-6 hours	2-4 hours	6-10 mins per chop or steak
Poultry			
	Minimum of	Minimum of	
Birds 3 Kg and over (6.6lb)	24 hours 5-8 hours per 450g	9 hours $2^1/_2$-$3^1/_2$ hours per 450g	9-12 mins per 450g
Birds under 3 Kg (6.6lb)	Minimum of 24 hours per 450g	Minimum of 9 hours per 450g	9-12 mins per 450g
Poultry portions	6-8 hours	Not recommended	6-10 mins per portion
Fish			
Whole fish or thick portions	4-5 hours per 450g	1-2 hours per 450g	5 mins per 450g
Fillets or thin flat fish	3-4 hours per 450g or cook from frozen	1-2 hours per 450g or cook from frozen	5 mins per 450g or cook from frozen
Vegetables	Cook from frozen		
Prepared Meals	Follow manufacturers instructions		

450g = 1lb

DRYING

Foods such as pasta, rice and pulses are all dried products. They have a long shelf life, if correctly stored, because micro-organisms cannot grow on them. Food drying is probably the oldest preservation process known to man. In hot countries, grains and fruits were traditionally sun-dried before storage. Fish has been dried naturally in the wind in colder climates for centuries. Modern processes include spray drying, freeze drying and tunnel drying. Sun drying is still used for some imported goods such as sea salt and spices.The main purpose of drying food is to lower its moisture content so as to prevent micro-organisms from growing, as micro-organisms require a supply of water in order to grow.

Q: What can go wrong with dried food?

A: The major problem with dried food is that if it is not correctly stored, moisture can build up which can lead to the growth of micro-organisms. Oxidation, the process whereby the food may react with oxygen in the air and produce off-flavours or colour changes can take place. This may also lead to losses of nutrients such as vitamin C. Browning may take place because of caramelisation, (the chemical dehydration of sugars), or because certain proteins and sugars in the food combine to form brown or black coloured compounds. This may alter both the taste and the rehydration properties of the food. Enzymic changes may also take place due to active natural compounds (enzymes) in the food. These reactions do not usually occur if the food has been correctly prepared and sufficiently dried. Dried foods should always be stored in an airtight container in a cool, dry place. If correctly stored many of these changes can be prevented and deterioration of the food slowed down.

Dried foods should not be stored in potentially damp cupboards, for example, above a steaming kettle. Some dried food especially cheap imports from less developed countries may contain foreign bodies such as twigs, stones and sand. Always buy from a reputable supplier.

Q: How long can dried food be stored?

A: Always examine the packet thoroughly for any recommendation made by the manufacturer. If no best before date appears the following list can be used as a guide.

Pasta	12 months
Rice	12 months
Pulses	12 months
Flours (Plain)	12 months (usually date coded)
Flours with raising agents	6 months (usually date coded)
Dried Fruit	6 months (usually date coded)

Open packets of dried goods should be transferred to a clean, dry, airtight container. It is a good idea to retain the date mark from the packet or make a note on the container when you bought the product.

CANNING

The principle behind canning food is quite simple. Food is sealed in an air tight container and is cooked whilst inside the container to make the produce inside sterile. The cooking process takes place in a large pressure cooker known as a retort. The time and temperature required for cooking is calculated according to the size of the container and the type of food inside it. At the end of the cooking process the food is cooled quickly and then stored at room temperature. The cooking process kills all micro-organisms able to grow in the food, and the container prevents any other organisms from recontaminating the food.

Q: How long can canned food be stored?

A: Most undamaged cans which are stored in a cool dry place will remain perfectly safe for about 4 to 5 years. However, the quality of the contents will slowly deteriorate. If no date is given on the product by the manufacturer we suggest the following storage times.

Canned Meat and Fish

Corned Beef	Use within 5 years
Salmon	Use within 5 years
Fish in Oil	Use within 5 years
Fish in Brine or Tomato	Use within 3 years
Other meats	Use within 3 years

Canned Fruit and Vegetables

Pulses, Peas and Beans	Use within 4 years
Mushrooms	Use within 4 years
Sweetcorn	Use within 3 years
Carrots	Use within 3 years
Spinach	Use within 3 years
Unpeeled Potatoes	Use within 3 years
Pineapple	Use within 3 years
Most deciduous fruits (eg peaches)	Use within 3 years
Tomatoes	Use within 2 ½ years
Baked Beans	Use within 2 years
Peeled Potatoes	Use within 2 years
Citrus fruit (eg mandarins)	Use within 2 years
Soft fruit (eg raspberries)	Use within 2 years
Apples	Use within 2 years

Canned Ready Meals

Sauces and Soups	Use within 1 year
Ready Meals	Use within 1 year

Canned Dairy Products

Evaporated Milk	Use within 6 months
Condensed Milk	Use within 6 months
Rice pudding	Use within 6 months
Canned Carbonated Drinks	Use within 6 months

Q: How should cans be stored?

A: Cans should be stored in a cool dry cupboard, and should not be used if they are dented, or rusty, particularly on the seal. If the can has 'blown' (that is if the shape is distorted) you should be especially careful. A distorted shape may indicate that the product is not up to standard or that micro-organisms producing gases are present. These organisms may be pathogenic ie producing harmful substances. The can and contents should be disposed of. ***Do not attempt to open it***.

If when opening a can, food spurts out, do not use the contents. Throw away the can and clean up the mess - wash the can opener and all surfaces involved with a detergent solution.

Q: How should canned food be treated once open?

A: Once opened, canned food should be treated as fresh. Remove the contents from the can and store it in a clean dry container. Never store part of the contents in the opened can as this may lead to increased uptake of metal (see Chapter XIII). Canned food has already been cooked which means that if bacteria infect the product once it is opened the bacteria will flourish. Try to use the contents of the can as soon as possible. Two days is a good guide for most canned foods.

Q: What is the maximum time I should keep foods such as sauces in the cupboard?

A: In response to consumer demand many foods such as Mayonnaise, Spicy Sauces and Ketchup now contain fewer preservatives but as a result they now require refrigeration. Check the instructions on the label to see if refrigeration is required. If refrigeration is not required and no other instructions are given these products are normally safe in a cool dry cupboard for one month from the date of opening.

FOOD IRRADIATION

Q: What is food irradiation?

A: Food irradiation is a processing treatment applied to food. Irradiation is produced in one of two ways. It may be from an electron beam machine, which can generate beams of electrons or X-rays, or generated as gamma-rays from radioisotopes such as cobalt 60. The process involves passing the food through the radiation field at a set speed to control the amount of energy or dose absorbed by the food. At no time does the food come into contact with the radioactive source of gamma radiation and the process does not render the food radioactive.

Irradiation produces benefits such as destroying the pathogens responsible for food borne illnesses, destroying insect pests in grain and other foods, reducing microbiological load in spices, delaying sprouting in potatoes and onions and thus greatly extending the storage life of fresh food.

Q: When can we use food irradiation?

A: In order to maintain a food supply which is both safe and wholesome, man has developed various methods of food preservation to control food spoilage, food borne diseases and insect infestations. These include drying, salting and smoking which have subsequently been supplemented with freezing, refrigeration, canning, pasteurisation and chemical treatment. FOOD IRRADIATION provides an alternative to, and extends our methods of, preservation.

We know that some raw foods can contain food poisoning organisms amongst their normal microbial flora. To make food safer, as well as more enjoyable, we have learned to cook food. This use of heat may be mild, as in pasteurisation typically at 72 degrees Celsius for 15 seconds or more severe 121-140 degrees Celsius for canned or UHT foods. Irradiation is used in a similar way and is another tool to protect us from bacteria which are ever present in our environment and which are always present in our food, no matter how good the level of hygiene and the manufacturing process.

Q: Is it safe?

A: The weight of scientific opinion considers food irradiation to be a safe process, and another useful tool for protecting our food. It is not a panacea however, and will not eradicate all bacteria by itself. Food irradiation is to be seen as a partner with good manufacturing practice, good hygiene, packaging and temperature control. Irradiation has been studied since 1905, and no other food processing method has been subject to such close examination for so many years. Whilst some individual scientists may have reservations, the weight of scientific opinion agree it to be a safe process.

Food irradiation has been accepted by the World Health Organisation since 1961, the Food and Agriculture Organisation, and the International Atomic Energy Agency who evaluated the process and their Joint Expert Committee on Food Irradiation declared that the use of food irradiation up to a specific dose of 10kGy is a safe process (when applied at recommended doses). In the United Kingdom, the Advisory Committee on Irradiation and Novel Foods reported in 1986 that food irradiation is a safe process, presenting no toxicological hazard and introducing no special nutritional microbiological problem.

Q: Why use irradiation?

A: All food contains bacteria. It is well known that some foods can contain food poisoning organisms amongst their normal microbial flora. Campylobacter jejuni and Salmonella are ever present in animals and from there, spread throughout the environment. Listeria monocytogenes is common on vegetation and presents a problem to those who are immuno-suppressed (those whose immune systems are weak). Pasteurisation and other methods are ways of controlling bacterial level, thereby increasing safety margins. Irradiation enables this to be achieved while having minimal effects on the nature and quality of food.

Q: What are the benefits of irradiation?

A: The potential benefits of irradiation include:

Improving food safety
Medium dose food irradiation, acts like pasteurisation and can kill live food poisoning bacteria, in particular the three which have recently caused concern - Salmonella, Campylobacter jejuni and Listeria monocytogenes. At Government suggested levels of 10kGy, irradiation does not destroy viruses, preformed toxins in food, nor does it make the food sterile. For example, spices in their normal commercial state carry high and sometimes dangerous bacterial loads which will contaminate the foods in which they are used. Currently some spices cannot be treated by heating as this destroys the flavours for which they are used. The old method of treating spices by fumigation with ethylene oxide, has been banned by the EEC due to its possible carcinogenic properties. The irradiation of spices would now eliminate the need for chemical treatments.

Reducing spoilage and wastage

Food irradiation can help reduce food wastage by preventing insect attack on cereal and other grains, mould production on fruits and other foods, sprouting of crops (such as potatoes) which are stored for long periods, and arresting the ripening process of some fruits.

The irradiation process is not suitable for all foods because of its effect on taste. Foods such as fatty fish or some dairy products are unsuitable for irradiation due to their high fat content. Irradiating fatty foods will accelerate the normal production of rancidity and the food's taste would be severely and detrimentally affected. Where there is no effect on taste, irradiation is suitable for use on poultry, some seafoods, spices and some fruits and vegetables allowing some tropical and soft fruits such as strawberries to be harvested nearer to their maturity, and making them available out of season.

Q: What do we know about food irradiation?

A: Food irradiation is not a new form of food preservation, it was introduced some eighty years ago. Major research on sterilisation of food was carried out in several countries some thirty years ago. Animals on sterile diets have been fed all-irradiated food diets over many years and generations without any ill effects. In British hospitals, patients in intensive care who are immuno-suppressed, such as transplant patients, have been given sterile irradiated food for more than twenty years in order to prevent infection.

Q: Is food irradiation used in other countries?

A: Food irradiation is currently permitted in 37 countries worldwide, including 7 member states of the EC, and the United States of America. It is already in use in over 21 of these countries principally for the reduction or elimination of dangerous micro-organisms in food.

The process is widely practiced with great success, in many countries, including Russia (cereals), South Africa (fruit and vegetables), Belgium (spices and food ingredients), The Netherlands (frozen fish and seafood), Hungary (onions and paprika), Norway (spices), and the United States of America (foods such as dried or dehydrated aromatic vegetables spices and herbs).

Q: Will irradiation make food radioactive?

A: No. All foods contain an element of radioactivity and irradiation will not significantly change the level of radioactivity.

Q: Does Irradiation make spoiled food good and does irradiated food keep forever?

A: No. Food irradiation is not magic. It is a useful process, which can be used in selected cases. Just as pasteurised milk does not keep forever, and still needs to be packaged and handled hygienically at chill temperatures, so too does irradiated food. If food already tastes or smells bad or 'off' before irradiation, it cannot be 'saved' by irradiation - the bad taste or sour taste will remain. Just as we cook to make raw food safe to eat, the use of irradiation should mean that less food poisoning organisms are brought into the kitchen. There is evidence that some spoilage bacteria are resistant to irradiation and that these will limit the shelf life of irradiated food.

Q: What about vitamin loss and the nutritional value of irradiation?

A: Some vitamins, particularly A and E, thiamin, pyridoxine, and ascorbic acid are reduced by irradiation. Losses are small when irradiation doses are kept to within the permitted range and generally are comparable with other food processes and techniques. If vitamin losses were significant, we could use this as a method for testing for irradiated food.

Q: How do we know if food is irradiated or not?

A: Generally the changes caused by food irradiation are very small. It is for this reason that it has been difficult to find ready methods to detect whether food has been irradiated. The limited degree of chemical change induced, has so far prevented the development of a simple, unambiguous test to distinguish irradiated from unirradiated foods.

Q: Will irradiation eliminate Clostridium botulinum?

A: Irradiation will kill vegetative cells of Clostridium botulinum. However, the required dose to kill its heat resistant spores would be 50kGy. This level of dose produces quite unacceptable changes in the colour and flavour of the treated food. Hence at a level of irradiation of 10kGy Clostridium botulinium will not be completely eliminated. However, many other processes will not remove it. Pasteurisation, for example, does not totally eliminate Clostridium botulinium. Spores such as those of Clostridium botulinium will therefore still be present even after irradiation. However, their presence will not result in food poisoning, the problem arises when the spores germinate and grow to produce the toxins. We therefore must prevent germination and growth. To do this food must be kept chilled or we must increase the acidity level of the food.

Q: Will the elimination of certain micro-organisms through irradiation allow other food poisoning micro-organisms to flourish?

A: There is no evidence for competition between micro-organisms in food, apart from fermented foods eg. yoghurt, cheese, salami, when the growth of food pathogens is prevented by the growth of the fermenting organism. The use of irradiation should result in the killing of food poisoning organisms so that fewer are brought into the kitchen or are present in the food.

Q: What do we need?

A: Obviously as consumers we wish to know more about all aspects affecting the safety of food. The FSAC believes it is essential that consumers are given the choice of whether to purchase irradiated food or not.

Clear labelling
Clear labelling is a pre-requisite of such choice and so too is a clear supervision of the irradiation process itself, so that food and its components are only irradiated once. This is why any irradiation plant intending to irradiate food for sale in this country must first obtain a licence from the Ministry of Agriculture Fisheries and Food (MAFF) and any food ingredient that has been irradiated must be clearly labelled with either 'Treated with ionising radiation' or 'Irradiated'.

The effect on agrichemical residues
There is little research data available on the likely effects irradiation may have on agrichemical residues which may be present on the surface of the fruit and vegetables presented for treatment. The Government Advisory Committee on Irradiated and Novel Foods acknowledged this absence of data and recommended that MAFF set up a research programme to assess such effects. Although the results from this research are not yet available, The Government Advisory Committee on Irradiated and Novel Foods expect there to be little effect on agrichemical residues.

Q: Is food irradiation permitted in the United Kingdom?

A: Yes. Food irradiation has been a permitted process for specific foods in the United Kingdom since 1991.

Q: Are there any restrictions on food irradiation?

A: Yes. If a processing company wished to irradiate food in the UK it must apply to the Ministry of Agriculture Fisheries and Food for a licence.

A licence is granted to the operator of the processing plant only if MAFF are satisfied with the standard of the plant. The licence if granted is specific to the purpose for which the application was made and for the particular food categories specified. In 1991, one licence application was granted for the irradiation of herbs and spices. This licence was revised in 1992 to extend the range of herbs and spices that could be irradiated. No other licences have been granted to date.

Q: What about imported food products?

A: Any company that wished to export irradiated food to the UK would also have to apply to the Ministry of Agriculture Fisheries and Food for a licence, they would be subject to inspection by MAFF, and would have to comply to the same standards applied to processors in this country.

Q: What happens after the licence is granted?

A: The licence is granted for a fixed term and the operator is continually subject to inspection and review by the Ministry of Agriculture, Fisheries and Food. Any failure to comply with the terms of the licence may result in its removal and prosecution of the operator.

Q: How can you tell if food has been irradiated?

A: Any food that has been irradiated must be clearly labelled with either the words 'Treated with ionising radiation' or 'Irradiated'. Similarly any irradiated ingredient in a product must be clearly labelled in the ingredients listing. However, any minor component of an ingredient that makes up less than 25% of the finished product, eg irradiated herbs in a salami used to top a pizza, will not have to be labelled if it has been irradiated. This exemption is currently being debated at international level by the member states of the European Community.

VETERINARY MEDICINE AND FEED ADDITIVES

Q: What is a Veterinary Medicine?

A: Veterinary medicines are substances that may be administered to an animal for the treatment or prevention of disease. Veterinary medicinal products also include vaccines and vitamin/mineral injections.

Q: What restrictions are there on the use of veterinary medicines?

A: A veterinary medicine must be licensed under the Medicines Act. A licence is only granted if a product is shown to be safe, effective and of standard quality. The conditions of the licence will state how the medicine is to be applied and will specify a withdrawal period prior to slaughter, during which all medication must cease if the animal is intended for food use.

Approximately one hundred product applications were received during 1991-92. Over this same period sixty five products were granted a licence. However it is difficult to compare these figures directly due to the way in which the applications are processed. On average an application can take between 1 and 3 years to process, and of course many years to produce the data required.

Q: How are new products assessed prior to being licenced?

A: Applications for new product licences are made to the Veterinary Medicines Directorate (VMD), which was set up in April 1989. A similar body handled applications prior to 1989. Part of the Directorate's remit is to assess applications for animal medicines, issue licences and monitor suspected adverse reactions. The licence which allows the medicinal product to be marketed is granted only after the product has undergone a rigorous assessment, and has satisfied the Veterinary Products Committee's (VPC) criteria for new products.

A company seeking a licence for a product will present all the data it has gathered to the VMD for examination. The data must include information on efficacy, quality and safety. If the data are incomplete the company will be advised and their application will be returned. The VPC meets every month to consider novel licence applications and appeals. Applications considered by the VPC include products that claim to prevent or treat disease and products that may be administered by injection, by mouth, by application to the skin or by addition to feed. Members of the VPC are independent and are appointed for their expertise in veterinary medicine, toxicology, pharmacy, microbiology, physiology, medicine and other disciplines relevant to animal and human health or the environment.

Applications are assessed by a veterinarian, a pharmacist, and a toxicologist in the VMD, and then referred to one of two scientific committees in the VMD who work to guidelines agreed with the VPC. Both of these committees and the VPC may call for additional expertise that may be necessary to assess an application.

If the application satisfies the standards set by the VPC then approval is given and a licence will be issued. If the application fails to meet the licensing criteria or is unsatisfactory in any way it is referred to the VPC. New or novel chemicals are referred by the VMD committees to the VPC.

If after further consideration the VPC is satisfied with an application, a licence will be issued by the VMD. If the application is unsuccessful the applicant company is informed. The company may then request a formal oral or written hearing before the VPC and provide any additional information required. If the VPC is satisfied with the application after the formal hearing it will recommend to the Licensing Authority that a Licence be granted. Otherwise it recommends that the application is refused.

The company can then make a final representation to the Medicines Commission, a statutory body constituted under the Medicines Act to advise the Licensing Authority, who will make its recommendation after a formal hearing.

Q: Who checks that veterinary medicines are not being abused?

A: In the UK the State Veterinary Service. Random samples of meat are taken as part of the National Surveillance Scheme for Residues in Meat.

Over 45,000 samples were taken during 1991 of which only 172 samples were above the Maximum Residue Levels (MRL's) - the level at which action is required to reduce residue.

Q: What is a maximum residue limit?

A: The levels of residue permitted, following the application of veterinary medicines, are controlled by the setting of maximum residue limits (MRL). The MRL is always much less than the average Acceptable Daily Intake (ADI). The MRL's are based on what is achievable using Good Agricultural Practice and are assessments of the maximum residues that should result when veterinary medicines are properly used. When MRL's are set, safety factors are built in to ensure that the level is significantly below the level that is known to have an adverse effect.

Q: What is an acceptable daily intake (ADI)?

A: By definition, the ADI is that amount which can be consumed by humans daily for a lifetime, without appreciable risk. It is derived from the doses which cause no adverse effects in experimental studies to which a large safety factor is applied. The ADI covers exposure from all sources and at all ages.

Q: Are samples with residue levels above the MRL safe?

A: This will depend on how large the residue is. MRL's are meant as a guideline for good agricultural practice. If MRL's are exceeded this is an indication that the farmer should modify his procedure.

Of 45 000 samples taken by the National Surveillance Scheme, 172 samples did have a residue level that exceeded the MRL. However, the levels did not exceed the ADI (Acceptable Daily Intake) and were significantly below levels that could be considered hazardous to human health.

Q: Are there any restrictions on the farmer for the administration of veterinary medicines?

A: Yes. Certain medicines, prescription only, may only be administered by a vet or as directed by the vet and under his supervision. This category of medicines is only available from a vet or from a pharmacy with a prescription from the attending vet.

Medicines, other than above, may only be purchased from an approved, authorised source, such as a vet, a pharmacist or a registered distributor. The farmer must comply with any recommended withdrawal periods for the animal. The sale for slaughter of an animal before the end of its withdrawal period is illegal. Records must be kept of all veterinary medicines administered including those administered in animal feed.

Q: What is a withdrawal period?

A: A withdrawal period for a product is the period of time before slaughter during which veterinary medicine must not be given to the animal. The withdrawal period allows for the veterinary medicine to clear from the animal's system. This may either be by metabolism, passing through the digestive system or by excretion or a combination of them.

Withdrawal periods ensure that meat and meat products from animals which have received veterinary medicine are safe. At present the standard withdrawal periods used when there is not a defined period for a drug are:
28 days meat from poultry and mammals including fat and offal
7 days milk
7 days eggs

Q: What happens after the licence is granted?

A: Veterinary medicines or feed additives undergo continual monitoring by both the Ministry of Agriculture, Fisheries and Food and scientists within the European Community. Whenever any new evidence on a specific veterinary medicine or feed additive arises from this critical review, its licence and/or its use, will be questioned. Only if it is still considered safe for the animal, the manufacturer, the administrator, the farmer and ultimately the consumer will the use of the product still be permitted. Failure on any aspect will mean that the veterinary medicine will be banned or that the additive will not be permitted for use in animal feed.

The Joint FAO/WHO Expert Committee on Food Additives at regular meetings also carry out toxicological evaluation of certain veterinary drug residues in food. This committee serves as a scientific advisory body to FAO, WHO, their member states and the Codex Alimentarius Commission. They accomplish their task by preparing reports of their meetings, publishing specifications and toxicological graphs on the substances they have considered.

Q: What are feed additives?

A: Feed additives, as the name suggests, are substances added to animal feed and are quite distinct and different from food additives. They are a very useful means of administering medicines to groups of animals without the stress of handling them individually.

A feed additive may be for example a nutritional supplement such as vitamins or minerals or veterinary products to prevent or treat disease. Feed additives also include compounds which prevent deterioration of the feeds eg. antioxidants and can be preservatives.

Q: What controls exist when Veterinary medicines are used as feed additives?

A: If the substance used is a therapeutic (disease curing) or prophylactic (disease preventing) drug, its administration must take place under veterinary direction and the necessary precautions undertaken at time of manufacture and feeding, and with strict adherence to withdrawal times.

Q: Can hormones be used to promote growth in an animal?

A: No. The use of hormones as growth promoters was prohibited for food production in the UK and in the rest of the EC in January 1987. Any product imported into the UK must comply with British Food Law and so only meat raised without the use of hormones can be imported for sale.

Q: If antibiotics can be used in animal feed, does this mean that microorganisms can build up a resistance to them?

A: It is known that pathogenic bacteria can mutate and become resistant to antibiotics. For this reason, antibiotics that have human or veterinary therapeutic applications are not permitted for general use as a feed additive.

Q: Once a product licence is granted, is it ever renewed?

A: A product licence is valid for five years after which time it must be reviewed. Extra data may be required to support this renewal. A facility also exists to question a product licence before the end of five years if a problem becomes apparent. There is at present a major review of licences within the EC and most of the process should be completed by the end of 1993.

BOVINE SOMATOTROPIN (BST)

Q: What is BST?

A: Bovine Somatotropin (BST) is a natural protein hormone produced by the pituitary gland in all dairy cows. (This should not be confused with BSE (see chapter VI.) The function of BST is to promote milk yield by helping direct the flow of feed nutrients into the production of milk. BST is found naturally at very low levels in all milk.

Q: Can BST be synthesised (Manufactured)?

A: Yes. BST can be synthesised by a process similar to fermentation by micro-organisms that have been genetically engineered.

Q: Is BST used in this country?

A: At present synthesised BST is available only for use in limited trials which are being undertaken under the scrutiny of the Veterinary Products Committee. Although licence applications have been made for two products, these have been, to date, rejected by the Veterinary Products Committee. There is currently no product licence available.

Q: Is BST used in other countries?

A: All members of the European Community and many other countries are also examining the use of BST through trails but there is moratorium on its use in the

EC. The Committee for Veterinary Medical Products (CVMP), who advise the European Commission, consider the use of BST to be a safe way to increase milk production. The issue, however, of animal welfare is still raising concerns.

Q: Is BST found in the milk of trial animals?

A: BST occurs at very low levels in the milk of all cows whether treated or not. The amounts found in milk from cows receiving supplemented BST are not outside the natural limits of untreated cattle. The quality of milk from treated cows is the same as that of normal milk.

Q: How can you be sure that the milk you are buying is from cattle which have not been treated?

A: The only dairy cattle in Britain treated with BST are the very small numbers of cattle taking part in the trials (less that 1/10,000 dairy farms in the trial). The milk from these trials however will be pooled with milk collected from farms not in the trial. The farms taking part in the trials are not allowed to disclose this information to the public. However, those not participating are able to disclose that they are not taking part.

Q: Is BST safe for the consumer?

A: Yes. BST is safe for consumers. It is a protein hormone specific in its action in cattle. It is broken down, as are the other proteins, in the digestive tract of the human body and is therefore inactive after consumption.

Q: Is BST likely to be used by all dairy farmers in the future?

A: The European Community has placed a moratorium on the general use of BST within the Community until the end of December 1993. If BST is approved for use after this date each member state will have to decide if it wishes to allow the use of the product in its national market.

In the UK the Government's Veterinary Products Committee has made a recommendation that BST is not used for British milk production. The Committee is not fully satisfied with the results of animal welfare tests, but states that it has found no evidence to indicate that BST poses any threat to human health or the environment.

As with all licenced products the choice whether to use BST or not, (should a licence be granted) will remain with the farmer.

CLENBUTEROL

Q: What is Clenbuterol?

A: Clenbuterol is one of the group of substances classified as beta agonists. It is licenced for use as a veterinary treatment in respiratory disease in horses, and respiratory disease and calving problems in cattle.

Q: Why are some people concerned about Clenbuterol?

A: A number of reports indicate that Clenbuterol may have been used illegally in Ireland, Spain and other countries as a repartitioning agent: to increase the lean content of an animal carcass and reduce the fat content. When used illegally for this purpose, the doses required would be much higher than those used for therapeutic use. As part of the National Surveillance Scheme regular monitoring for veterinary medicine residues including clenbuterol is undertaken for U.K. produced meat.

Q: Is Clenbuterol found in meat?

A: No: when administered correctly under veterinary supervision. The withdrawal period i.e. specified length of time prior to slaughter when the drug must not be administered, ensures that the drug is cleared from the body.

Q: How can illegal use of Clenbuterol be detected?

A: The illegal use of Clenbuterol may be detected prior to slaughter by ante mortem veterinary inspection. Through Ante Mortem Inspection suspect animals are identified by changes in body shape. Tests can, and are carried out under the Residues Regulations, on animals administered or having been given Clenbuterol illegally. If there is any suspicion that Clenbuterol has been used, the animal or meat is withheld. If proved to be contaminated with Clenbuterol, the meat will be banned from human consumption and destroyed.

Q: What safeguards are taken to ensure meat is safe?

A: If during a veterinary inspection at an abattoir, the veterinarian observes characteristics such as:
▷ change in shape and size of the animal
▷ blocky muscling (a veterinary term which describes animals that are very muscular)
▷ or the animal may be in some distress or tremoring

The veterinarian will detain the animal on the suspicion of Clenbuterol use, preventing its slaughter. Samples will be taken for laboratory examination for the presence of Clenbuterol.

In addition over 400 samples of cattle and pig liver and bile have been tested for beta agonists (the group of chemicals to which Clenbuterol belongs). To date, no positive samples have been found in Great Britain. Any imported products brought into this country must comply with The Food Safety Act 1990 and in particular The Animal, Meat, Meat Products (Examination for Residues and Maximum Residue Limits) Regulations 1991 and so would be subject to inspection.

Q: Is it true that Clenbuterol causes ill effects such as muscle pain, palpitations and nervousness in humans?

A: In reports from Spain where liver (which accumulates Clenbuterol more than muscle) was eaten from animals illegally treated with very high levels of Clenbuterol, a number of people did become ill with symptoms similar to those described above. These reported cases were the direct result of illegal food adulteration. Clenbuterol can be used to treat humans and the above effects are not present in normal therapeutic levels.

The Regulatory Authorities seek to prevent any such incidents in this country through the on-going observation and surveillance programmes and the application of legislation such as Food Safety Act and in particular The Animals, Meat and Meat Products (Examination for Residues and Maximum Residue Limits) Regulations 1991 and there have been no reports of such findings in the UK.

Q: Is Clenbuterol accumulated in the animal's body?

A: Clenbuterol is quickly excreted and so once administration stops, the product will clear from the body. Once excreted, the product is no longer present to pose a toxic threat to humans. Following therapeutic use Clenbuterol is cleared from the animal's body in 3-5 days. The standard withdrawal period is 28 days for meat, well in excess of the time required for the drug to be cleared from the animal.

Q: How effective is the test for Clenbuterol?

A: The test is reliable and can detect minute traces of the drug. Detection is possible down to levels below the proposed maximum residue level (MRL) of 0.5 parts per billion. If less than one particle in every 2 billion is present it will be detected. If samples of liver are taken these will act as a good indicators of malpractice. Sampling is rigorously carried out by authorised officers who follow a statutory code of practice.

BOVINE SPONGIFORM ENCEPHALOPATHY (BSE)

BOVINE SPONGIFORM ENCEPHALOPATHY (BSE)

Q: What is Bovine Spongiform Encephalopathy? (BSE) (Mad Cow Disease)

A: Bovine Spongiform Encephalopathy (BSE) is a slowly progressive and ultimately fatal nervous disorder of adult cattle. It was first described by Wells and others in 1986 in the Veterinary Record. A few suspect cases in 1985 and 1986 increased to between 250-300 cases a week in 1990 and there are currently around 600-700 cases per week.

Having been previously healthy and of good body size the affected cows become weak, edgy and irritable, they begin to lose co-ordination of their limbs and may eventually become very aggressive. The brains of infected animals are damaged, with holes in certain parts of the brain tissue, giving it a chacteristic spongy look when viewed under the microscope.

All the available evidence suggests that BSE belongs to a group of progressive, degenerative diseases of the central nervous system known as the spongiform encephalopathies caused by a group of conventional transmissible agents. Other similar diseases include Scrapie in sheep, transmissible mink encephalopathy, Creutzfeldt-Jakob Disease (CJD) in humans and feline spongiform encephalopathy in cats.

Q: What is the cause of BSE? Where did it come from?

A: The Report of the Working Party on BSE (Southwood Committee) published in February 1989 concluded that BSE 'has appeared as a result of contamination of meat and bone meal derived from sheep offal and fed to British cattle from the early 1980's'.

Contamination may have arisen because modern rendering practices failed to destroy the agent of Scrapie. There was a ban on the use of ruminant protein in animal feed in 1988. To date there is no evidence of any other source of infection which would sustain the epizootic in cattle.

FEED PROCESSING

Animal feeds usually contain a proportion of protein. This protein can be from various sources including soya, fish meal or meat and bone meal. Animal feed is sold guaranteeing a certain proportion of protein.

In the late 70's some rendering plants changed their method of processing carcasses into meat and bone meal for animal feeds. They adopted a system of continuous processing which may have resulted in lower temperatures being reached. At the same time the use of solvents such as benzenes, to remove excess fats from the meat and bone meal was reduced. As a result the final heating stage to remove the solvents, involving very high temperatures was lost. It is believed that the high temperature regime destroyed the Scrapie agent and the loss of this may have led to the BSE outbreak.

At the same time the number of sheep in the United Kingdom increased and with it the level of Scrapie. However research is currently being carried out in these areas to substantiate this.

P.S. Chernobyl Nuclear Accident happened 198

Q: Are pigs, poultry and pets still fed specified offal?

A: No. To prevent further infection in cattle, the use of ruminant based protein in ruminant feed was banned in July 1988 and now there is a ban on specified offal in all animal and pet foods. From November 1988 the specified offal of a cow were banned for human consumption. They include the brain, thymus, spleen, spinal cord, intestines and tonsils.

In the case of pigs it is worth noting that they have been fed animal protein derived from ruminants over many years without ill effects.

Also as a precautionary measure specified offal from healthy animals is now banned for use in the production of fertiliser.

Q: What happens to a cow with BSE?

A: From August 1988 all animals showing symptoms of BSE are slaughter and then disposed of, usually by incineration. No known BSE infected animal is slaughtered and then sold for human consumption. If an owner or agent suspects and animal has BSE, he/she must report this suspicion to the State Veterinary Service. The decision will then be made on whether the animal has BSE and the appropriate action taken by the State Veterinary Service.

The Advisory Panel of the FSAC has recommended that all infected cattle are incinerated or buried in quick lime to prevent infection of the water supply or soil. Now 80% of the suspected cases are incinerated.

Q: Does BSE occur elsewhere?

A: Cases of BSE have been reported in Eire and more recently in Switzerland and France. A disease with similar symptoms and clinical signs to BSE has been reported in the USA, where it is called downer cow syndrome (Gibbs et al; 1990).

A: Creutzfeldt-Jakob disease is a disease of humans and like other spongiform encephalopathies usually takes many years to incubate. The symptoms are loss of memory, and perhaps uncharacteristic behaviour, progressing to rapid mental deterioration, dementia, poor co-ordination and involuntary movements of limbs. No one knows how it is transmitted. The disease occurs worldwide, and affects one person in 2 million each year.

A: Scrapie has been present in British flocks for more than 250 years and is an obvious suspect as the source of infection. Scrapie is not a disease of young lambs. A number of epidemiological studies have failed to produce evidence of any link between CJD and potential exposure to Scrapie (Brown et al; 1979, Masters et al; 1979, Brown 1980; Chatelain et al; 1981).

A most remarkable incidence of CJD was reported among Libyan Jews in Israel in whom the incidence of CJD was more than 30 times greater that the world average. Because sheep eyeballs, brain and spinal cord are culinary delicacies for this ethnic group it was suggested that CJD could be associated with eating of Scrapie infectivity. However, it is known that members of Mediterranean and North African populations who emigrated to Israel and consume the same tissues do not have an increased frequency of CJD.

There are as many cases of CJD in Australia and New Zealand where there is no scrapie as there are in Britain and France where Scrapie is present.

In a cluster of cases of CJD which occurred in Czechoslovakia (Mayer et al; 1977) a familial tendency has been demonstrated and yet scrapie has not been recognised in that country for at least 100 years.

A: Yes. Beef is safe to eat. All cattle under the age of 2 years have never been fed meat and bone meal, the most likely cause of the disease. Before the ban approximately 80% of cattle over the age of 2 years were not fed meat and bone meal. All suspected cattle are slaughtered, the brain is examined for signs of infection, and the body is destroyed. The BSE agent, if present, is found in specified offal of a cow. As a precautionary measure all the specified offals are now removed from all animals over the age of 6 months after slaughter and prohibited from entering the human food chain. This precaution removes any offal in which the agent MIGHT remain.

Q: Is milk affected?

A: Milk has never been shown to transmit any form of spongiform encephalopathy. When a cow has BSE the milk yield drops and the cows are not able to be milked due to changes in behaviour.

The Southwood Committee stated that 'transmission of BSE via milk is very unlikely'. When an animal is diagnosed as likely to have BSE it is subsequently slaughtered. The milk from the animal, as soon as it is suspected of having BSE is destroyed and so prevented from entering the human food chain.

Q: What steps are currently being taken to combat BSE?

A: In 1988, the Ministry of Agriculture commissioned an independent working party, chaired by Professor Sir Richard Southwood, University of Oxford, to advise on what steps it should take to halt the epidemic and safeguard human health.

The Government made the disease BSE notifiable in June 1988, and as a result farmers must report any suspicion of BSE in their cattle. In the following month, the Government banned the practice of feeding cattle animal feed containing ruminant derived protein. Since August 1988 all cattle suspected of having BSE are now slaughtered and the carcass is incinerated or buried in quick lime. In November 1989, the Government banned specified offal from all cattle from entering the human food chain. These offals including the brain, spinal cord, thymus, tonsils and spleen are now removed immediately after slaughter from all bovine animals, over 6 months of age.

Following the advice of the Southwood Committee, the Tyrrell Committee chaired by virologist David Tyrrell, was set up to advise on further research into BSE and related diseases. Following the first report of the Tyrrell Committee, the Government has set up an £18 million research programme to look at BSE.

Q: What information has been gained so far from the research into BSE and related Diseases?

A: Horizontal transmission i.e. from cow to cow or bull:- Results indicate that this form of transmission is not a problem. In studies where one animal in a herd has contracted the disease there is no evidence of transmission to other members of the herd into which it comes into contact.

Vertical transmission i.e. from cow or bull to calf:- There is no evidence to suggest that the agent for BSE can be transmitted in sperm, therefore transmission from bull to calf is unlikely. No cases have been attributed to bull to calf transmission.

The Ministry of Agriculture, Fisheries and Food are currently undertaking research into maternal transmission of BSE in cattle. This project began in 1988 before the ruminant ban on animal feedstuffs and is not due for completion before 1995. The results to date show that although three cases of BSE have been confirmed within the experiment, the animals concerned were born before the ruminant feed ban. Thus any speculation as to the reason for this result would be premature.

As part of a further study 24 cases have been investigated by the Ministry of Agriculture where calves born to mothers who have BSE have later developed BSE themselves. With the exception of one of these cases, the cause of the disease may be attributed to factors such as the accidental feeding of pig or poultry feed. Pig and poultry feed could legally contain specified offal up to a later date than cattle feed.

If BSE can be transmitted vertically the incidence of this transmission seems to be low.

References:
Wells et al; 1987 Veterinary Record 121, 419
Gibbs et al; 1990 Lancet, May 26, 127
Brown et al; 1979 Annals of Neurology 6, 438
Masters et al; 1979 Annal of Neurology 5, 177
Brown; 1980 Epidemiological Reviews 2, 113
Chatelain et al; 1981 Journal of Neurological Science 51, 329
Mayer et al; 1977 Lancet 11, 256

FOOD ADDITIVES

Q: What are food additives?

A: Food additives are substances added to processed food often in small quantities that impart some additional qualities to the food. Each additive may have one or more of the following functions:

Preservative/Antioxidant. Enabling food to be kept more safely by preventing the food going rancid or by preventing the growth of bacteria and moulds.

Improve eating quality. Altering taste, texture, colour or nutritional value of the food.

Aid processing. Acting as emulsifiers, raising agents, anti-caking agents or stabilisers.

Q: Why do we need additives?

A: Firstly, without additives, many of the processed foods we eat could not be produced. For example, low fat margarines require emulsifiers, cakes require raising agents and bacon needs sodium nitrate and sodium nitrite for curing.

Secondly, without additives, the shelf-life of products would be much shorter. There would be more spoilage and waste, food would be inconsistent in quality, and it is also possible that food poisoning would become more frequent if products were stored beyond their shorter shelf life.

Q: Why not just use natural ingredients?

A: Many additives are natural, for example, one commonly used antioxidant is L-ascorbic acid (E300), better known as Vitamin C. Another example of a naturally occurring additive would be the preservative, benzoic acid, which occurs in fruits, sometimes at quite high levels, for example cranberries. However, not all functions performed by additives can be achieved by natural ingredients. Many naturally occurring colours and pigments in food are very sensitive to light and heat.

Processes such as canning which apply high temperature to the food for an extended period result in the natural colour being destroyed. This would result in, for example, canned peas being a khaki brown colour if artificial colourings were not added. In consumer trials such products have proved unpopular and there has been considerable consumer resistance to their appearance.

More importantly, the fact that a chemical is natural does not mean it is safe. There are many examples of natural substances that can be considered toxic (see Chapter I). Similarly, many natural foods are capable of bringing about allergic reactions in susceptible individuals. Foods such as strawberries, peanuts, milk and shellfish are all known to bring about allergic reactions in certain people.

Q: Do we need so many additives?

A: It may seem unnecessary to have so many different emulsifiers or varieties of colour but each additive has special properties which make it suited to different food uses. Before an additive is permitted for use, it must go through a long approval process. Evidence must be given that the additive is both safe and useful.

Q: What is an 'E' number?

A: Additives which are accepted as safe throughout the European Community are given an 'E' number. The 'E' number is simply a code that may be used to identify which additive has been used.

Q: Are additives safe?

A: Yes. The assessment procedure for additives is designed to ensure that they are safe before approval. It would be illegal to add any ingredient to food that would render it harmful or injurious to health.

Q: How are additives approved?

A: The approval procedure takes into account any tests that have already been conducted on the substance, and where gaps exist in the knowledge of this substance further tests are conducted. Even after approval, the additive is subject to a continuous review. For example, potassium bromate which was permitted for treatment of flour has recently been removed from the permitted list of food additives after it had been shown to be a carcinogen (cancer causing) in laboratory trials with rats.

Q: Who decides if an additive will be approved?

A: The process of approval is a thorough but complicated one. If a manufacturer develops an additive which is useful, they may carry out research to examine its properties and its safety. This research will then be examined by the Food Advisory Committee* which will examine the additive by a number of criteria;

1. Will it maintain or preserve the wholesomeness of food?
2. Will it extend dietary choice?
3. Will it supplement nutritional needs?
4. Will it improve preparation or storage of the food?
5. Will it improve the food's presentation?
6. Will it improve economic efficiency of production?

If the additive is found to be unnecessary then it will be rejected by the Food Advisory Committee. If, however, it is found to be useful, it will be examined by the Committee on Toxicology of Chemicals in Food, Consumer Products and the Environment (COT)‡.

The COT considers all the published research on the additive. They may consult other committees, research institutes or international organisations such as the World Health Organisation or European Community during this process. After this review the COT may recommend that the additive is:

▷ permitted

▷ is not permitted until further research is done, or

▷ permitted only if more information is made available.

The COT do not just recommend that an additive be permitted or not; they would also advise on the Acceptable Daily Intake for permitted additives.

The Food Advisory Committee considers the COT's advice and makes recommendations about the additive and its permitted uses.

The Secretary of State at The Department of Health, and Food Ministers at the Ministry of Agriculture, Fisheries and Food draw up regulations for the use of the additive. The proposed regulations are made public, and are open for public consultation. Consumers may make representations concerning the additive to the Food Safety Directorate Consumer Panel or through their local Member of Parliament.

If after this consultation procedure the additive is approved, the regulations will be signed jointly by the Ministers and laid before Parliament. Members of Parliament have a 40 day period in which to reject the regulations if necessary.

✱ Food Advisory Committee comprises:

Fifteen members who are all independent of the Government. Five emanate from consumer or law enforcement organisations, five from medical or academic professions, four are food industry representatives, & one is a retailing representative.

‡ **COT, Committee on Toxicology of Chemicals in Food, Consumer Products and the Environment comprises:**
Fourteen members who are all medical or scientific experts on harmful (toxic) substances. The European Community's process of approval runs in parallel to that of the UK.

Q: Do all additives have to go through this approval procedure?

A: The most important categories of food additives have already been through this approval procedure. These include:
▷ Preservatives
▷ Antioxidants
▷ Emulsifiers
▷ Stabilisers
▷ Colours
▷ Sweeteners

There are a number of categories that are just completing this long review and approval process, namely:
▷ Flavourings
▷ Flavour enhancers

The European Community aims to review all food additives in order to assure their safety. The review of flavour enhancers is likely to be completed by the end of 1993. The review of flavourings is not likely to be complete for some time due to the vast number of flavours, most of which are of natural origin. Natural flavourings include, for example, components of essential oils of herbs, spices and citrus fruits.

Q: What are the disadvantages of food additives?

A: As outlined above food additives serve many useful purposes. It must be remembered that certain individuals may have adverse reactions to an additive or additives and must be careful to avoid these substances. Clear labelling on foods containing additives is thus important. It is also important that the system for reviewing additives is maintained so that any new information on an additive can be scrutinised by the relevant committees.

COLOURING IN FOODSTUFFS

Colours in food initially seem to fall into two categories: either natural colours which are present in fresh food or added colour such as in canned peas or orange squash. However it is not quite as simple as that. Manufacturers often add 'natural' colours to food. These are not synthetic but are found in nature, and enhance the food's appearance. Manufacturers can make the claim 'containing no artificial colouring' if they are adding these natural colours.

Colouring can also be used in animal feeds. One example of this can be seen by comparing the colours of egg yolks. A deep orange colour is often thought to be healthy despite the fact that pale yolks are nutritionally the same. Hens that are free to peck their food from a variety of sources produce different coloured yolk varying from pale yellow to deep orange. Alternatively, hens that have been given a feed rich in coloured material such as corn are more likely to produce darker yolks. Egg producers can ensure orange yolks by feeding the hens with carotenes - orange or yellow plant pigments found naturally in most plants. A similar effect can be observed by comparing the colour of the flesh of chickens fed corn with those which are fed on other grains.

Q: Why are tinned peas coloured? What are they coloured with?

A: The heat processing of tinned peas turns the colour to greyish-green. Consumers generally prefer a bright green colour which makes the peas more attractive and appetising. Colouring such as E142, (Food Green S) are stable during heat processing and can be used to replace the lost colour.

Q: Is canned salmon artificially coloured?

A: No. There are several species of salmon whose flesh may vary in colour from pink to red.

Q: If salmon were fed artificial colours would this be declared on the label?

A: Canned salmon sold in this country has its origin indicated on the label, usually the Pacific ocean. The diet of salmon in the wild will naturally contain crustaceans, for example small shrimps. This diet affects the colour of the salmon's flesh, making it pink or orange. Therefore, there are no artificial colours in canned wild salmon.

Farmed salmon may be fed the peel or shells of shellfish to make the flesh pinker, or the fish's diet may be supplemented with coloured feed. These colourings are sometimes from plant origin or are manufactured to match natural chemicals. They are present only in very low levels in the fish flesh.

There is no legal requirement to declare the use of coloured feeds when farmed salmon is sold.

Q: Trout used to be white or cream-coloured, now it is often pink, why?

A: Farmed trout are sometimes fed with anthaxanthin or carotenes (a group of colourants) to make the flesh pink and therefore more attractive to the consumer.

Q: Are kippers and smoked cod dyed?

A: Modern smoking processes are designed more to make a product more appealing rather than preserve it. As a result a product such as smoked cod may only be lightly smoked for a mellow flavour and colour may be added after smoking. Tartrazine (E102) was, until recently, quite widely used. However, due to consumer resistance to this synthetic product, Annatto (E160(b)) a vegetable dye is now more popular. Oily fish such as kippers may be coloured with Brown FK which is added to the brine before smoking.

Q: Can you get kippers and other smoked fish which are dye free?

A: Yes. However, they are usually more expensive. Orange or yellow coloured fish are more appealing to consumers. Only specialist smoking houses avoid using colours in their smoking process.

PESTICIDES AND FOOD

Q: What are pesticides?

A: As the name suggests, pesticides are substances used to control pests in food production and storage. These pests may be micro-organisms (such as moulds or mildew), weeds, insects, birds or animals which cause losses, damage or contamination to food. The term 'pesticide' includes fungicides, insecticides, weedkillers, rodenticides and insect, bird or animal repellents.

The term pesticide and the regulation procedures applied to pesticides also embrace other 'agrichemicals' such as anti-sprouting agents and plant growth regulators. (Pesticides may also have other functions not related to food production, such as controlling insect vectors (carriers) of diseases like malaria, or the snails which carry bilharzia.)

Q: Why use pesticides?

A: The main reason for using pesticides is to minimise losses of food and to prevent spoilage. Without pesticides it has been estimated that up to one third of crops would be lost before harvest. Further losses could occur on storage due to vermin or moulds and rots. Reducing these losses and increasing yields helps to keep down prices.

By preventing spoilage during transportation and marketing, pesticides also play a part in ensuring that a variety of produce, from all over the world, is available throughout the year.

Properly used, pesticides can actually make foods safer. Fungicides help to control fungi (moulds and rots). Some of these moulds can produce highly toxic and carcinogenic metabolites (mycotoxins). Ergotism, the medieval 'St Anthony's Fire', is caused in this way and the mycotoxin, Aflatoxin B_1, is one of the most potent cancer causing compounds known to man.

Anti-sprouting agents, in addition to preventing losses of stored potatoes can also make the potatoes safer. When potatoes sprout they produce higher levels of some toxic compounds called Glycoalkaloids. These compounds namely solanine and chaconie are always present in potatoes but usually at low enough levels not to be hazardous; however, unacceptably high levels may accumulate when sprouting occurs.

Pesticides are used in the home to prevent disease-carrying pests like flies, cockroaches and mice contaminating food stored in the larder. Pesticides may perform the same role in improving food hygiene in stores.

Q: Do pesticides leave residues in foods?

A: Some pesticides, such as herbicides, would harm the crop if they were present in significant amounts. Other pesticides may leave detectable residues in the food. Some of the older pesticides were very persistent in the environment and in food, and the use of these on crops has been discontinued. Consequently, levels in the environment are now falling. Newer pesticides, such as the organophosphorus (OP) pesticides, or ethylene bisdithiocarbamate (EBDC) fungicides are less persistent and the levels in the field crops or stored crops fall rapidly after application. When properly used, the residual levels of pesticides are very low or even undetectable.

Q: Can the residues be removed by washing?

A. Some pesticides, such as EBDCs, are not absorbed by the plant but are only present on the surface. Generally, the residues of such pesticides may be reduced somewhat by washing or removed by peeling, although washing may be difficult with some leafy vegetables such as sprouts and peeling may be impractical with some vegetables like tomatoes. Some other pesticides are systemic, that is, they enter the cells of the plants and confer protection throughout, not just at points of initial contact. Such pesticides cannot be removed to any significant extent by washing.

Q: Are pesticides safe?

A: By their very nature pesticides are toxic to pests and may also be toxic to humans. However, some measure of selectivity is possible and pesticides are much more toxic to the pest, than they are to humans. Nevertheless, it has to be recognised that there is a potential risk to man (not least to the farmer applying the pesticide). Hence it is necessary to ensure that the extent and manner to which humans are exposed to pesticides is controlled in order to ensure safety.

Q: How do we know what are safe levels of residues?

A. Before any pesticide is approved for use it must undergo strict testing for toxicity, persistence and ecological risks.

The information from these tests is scrutinised by various national and international expert committees in the safety evaluation process. The major committees involved are the Advisory Committee on Pesticides in the United Kingdom, the Scientific Committee for Pesticides in the European Community and the Joint Food and Agriculture Organisation / World Health Organisation Meeting on Pesticide Residues at international level (the FAO and WHO are part of the United Nations Organisation).

On the basis of the scientific data, these Committees will determine 'Acceptable Daily Intakes' (ADIs) for pesticides. By definition, the ADI is that amount which can be consumed daily for a lifetime, without appreciable risk. It is derived from the doses which cause no adverse effects in experimental studies to which a large safety factor is applied. The ADI covers exposure from all sources and at all ages.

Q: What measures are taken to ensure that the ADI is not exceeded?

A: Only approved pesticides may be used in the UK and then only according to the provisions of the Control of Pesticides Regulations. Approval restricts uses to specific applications and limits the levels which can be applied. The levels of residues which result are controlled by the setting of Maximum Residue Limits (MRLs) for specific produce. The MRLs are based on what is achievable using Good Agricultural Practice, which are assessments of the maximum residues that should result when pesticides are properly used. The MRL is intended to ensure that only the necessary amount of pesticide is used. MRLs are not limits of safety but are intended to reduce levels of use to the minimum.

Q: What if MRLs are exceeded?

A: MRLs are set at such levels that even the intakes of those who consume vast amounts of particular foods should be well within the ADI. Consequently, if MRLs are occasionally exceeded to a small extent in any particular food, it does not mean that there is a risk to health.

Misuse of pesticides leading to MRLs being breached on a regular basis can result in prosecution with unlimited fines for those found guilty.

Recent surveys in the United Kingdom indicated that MRLs were rarely exceeded and that, in cases where the MRL's were exceeded the ADI would be unlikely to have been surpassed. The Committee on the Toxicity of Chemicals in Food, Consumer Products and the Environment reviewed the 34th report of the Steering Group on Food Surveillance (a report of the Working Party on Pesticide Residues 1988-90) and concluded that no hazard would result from even a consistent intake of extreme amounts of those foods containing the highest residue levels reported in the study. The Committee also found that the residue levels in most of the commodities analysed did not indicate any cause for concern.

Q: Are maximum residue levels laid down for all produce?

A: No. MRLs have been specified for a wide range of pesticides in many of the more important foods, including fruit and vegetables, cereals, meat and dairy produce, but the list is not complete and some commodities are not yet included. More MRLs are being established in the UK and in the European Community, where there is an active programme to standardise MRLs throughout the Community. MRLs are currently set at the lowest achievable level using good agricultural practice due to broad environmental concerns.

Q: What about imported produce?

A: Government regulations, which make it an offence to sell produce containing residues above the MRLs, apply to all imported foods. Food found to exceed MRLs can be confiscated and destroyed, whatever its origin.

Q: Who is policing these regulations?

A: The Food and Environment Protection Act and the more specific regulations mentioned above are enforced by local authorities together with the Health and Safety Executive and the Ministry of Agriculture, Fisheries and Food.

More generally, pesticide residues in food are kept under constant surveillance by the Working Party on Pesticide Residues of the Steering Group on Food Surveillance which also reports to the Advisory Committee on Pesticides. The latest Working Party Annual Report covered the period 1990 to 1991.

In addition diligent manufacturers and retailers also carry out their own targeted surveillance programmes to monitor levels of pesticide residues.

Q: Are there any steps being taken to reduce the use of pesticides?

A: Yes. Integrated crop management systems are being developed which employ combined strategies to control pests and reduce the use of agrochemicals. The strategies include planned crop rotation to minimise the build up of crop-specific pests, agricultural diversity rather than monoculture, and improved targeting of specific pests associated with particular crops.

Q: How can I tell which foods have been treated with pesticides?

A: You can't. There are currently no regulations which require produce to be labelled as such. However, beware of simplistic advice to avoid fruit or vegetables which look 'too perfect'. The presence of 'blemishes' is no guarantee that pesticides have not been used but, may, indeed, indicate mould infection, or that the produce is past its best.

Q: How can I avoid food produced using pesticides?

A: Many retailers are now stocking 'organically grown' produce which is grown without the deliberate application of pesticides, although it may not be possible to eliminate totally the traces of some of the older, persistent residues in the environment at the present time. A UK Register of Organic Food Standards has been drawn up which sets out rigorous national standards for organic foods. This is in line with a policy of allowing realistic choices to be made by the consumer.

ORGANIC PRODUCE

Q: What is organic produce?

A: Organic produce is food of produced using the principles of organic farming. These principles are as follows:
1. Using 'natural processes' for farming, for example, through increasing soil fertility by returning manure to the soil and avoiding the use of intensive chemical fertilisers.
2. Limiting use of chemicals for pest and weed control and using the alternatives such as carefully choosing resistant varieties of crops or rotating crops to prevent pests building up.

Q: Are there any controls on the growing and sale of organic produce?

A: Yes. On January 1st 1993 Regulations came into force to control the production and labelling of organic produce in the UK.

Q: Were there any Regulations before this?

A: No. Prior to this there was no legal definition for organic produce. The term organic referred to a number of voluntary systems operated by various groups such as the Soil Association.

Q: Who regulates the system?

A: The UK Register of Organic Food Standards (UKROFS), is the legal authority in the UK which enforces the European Council Regulations (EC Regulations 2092/91).

Q: Where did the Regulations come from?

A: The Regulations were adopted into British food law following discussions with the European Community.

Q: What do the Regulations cover?

A: The Regulations make it illegal to sell within the European Community products of plant origin, described as organic, unless they have been produced in accordance to the Regulations. In addition, registration is necessary for anyone who produces, prepares, imports or pre-packs organic produce.

These Regulations do not cover animal products. Regulations on organic animal products are currently being discussed but are unlikely to be implemented before 1994. The Regulations will examine areas such as animal welfare, the avoidance of medicines in treating sick animals, and the use of unconventional medicines such as homoeopathic drugs.

SOIL ASSOCIATION

Q: What is the Soil Association?

A: It is a charitable organisation, established in 1946, which maintains organic standards by inspecting growers' holdings and awarding its symbol to those who qualify. It commissions and publishes research into organic methods and advises and helps farmers and growers wishing to convert to organic production.

The Association helps to establish the distribution of organic food to local shops; provides expert advice to Government in Britain and overseas; and runs education programmes on organic farming for consumers and schools.

Q: What standards and criteria do organic farms follow?

A: Standards are based on a specification drawn up by the British Organic Standards Committee 1983, which include the prohibition of fertilisers in the form of soluble mineral salts and of agrochemical pesticides. The Soil Association's symbol is only awarded after the land has undergone a supervised conversion period of at least two years.

Q: Does the Soil Association symbol guarantee standards?

A: No. The symbol does not guarantee quality. It only indicates the produce has been organically grown.

Q: What other organisations are involved in setting standards for organically grown produce?

A: Other organisations include:- Organic Farmers and Growers Ltd, The Bio Dynamic Agricultural Association and Scottish Organic Producers Association.

The principles of these organisations are similar to those of the Soil Association. They aim to provide biological farmers with a service similar to that given by the Ministry of Agriculture, Fisheries and Food (MAFF) to conventional farmers.

In addition the European based federation - IFOAM (International Federation of Organic Agricultural Movements) has set guidelines for organic standards used by countries in Europe and the rest of the world. The IFOAM Logo cannot be used to promote products but as an organisation IFOAM provides advice to small associations wishing to produce and distribute organic produce.

WAX ON FRUIT

Q: Is washing in cold water enough to remove wax from fruit?

A: Wax on fruit is harmless. It is normally bees wax or carnuba wax from the leaf of the Brazilian wax palm. The wax gives the fruit an appealing glossy appearance and serves to prevent dehydration thereby extending its shelf life. The wax may also contain a fungicide which will prevent the food from spoiling quickly. Washing in cold water will not remove the wax nor will it significantly reduce the level of fungicide present. Provided however, that the level of fungicide present is at a level such that the ADI is not exceeded (see page VIII-3 for an explanation of ADI), the fruit will be perfectly safe to eat.

If you want to buy fruit without wax look for organic fruit. It is important to remember to always wash any fruit before eating to remove any soil and dust.

Q: Which fruits are waxed?

A: Whether a fruit is waxed or not depends partly on the variety of fruit and partly on the country of origin. For example, pears are unlikely to be waxed if they are British, South African or Chilean. However, some American producers do wax certain varieties. It is more likely that supermarket varieties in this country are unwaxed. The fruits most likely to be waxed are apples, avocados and citrus fruit (such as oranges, limes and lemons). Other fruits such as melons, plums, pears and pineapples may be waxed but the waxed varieties are not normally found on sale in this country.

ALAR

Q: What is Alar?

A: Alar is an agrochemical applied to orchard crops, such as apples and pears, as a growth regulator. Its function is to 'set' fruit, ie. help the tree to develop fruit of uniform size and prevent the fruit dropping before it is fully developed.

Q: Is Alar used in this country?

A: Alar is no longer manufactured or available for use in this country.

Q: What precautions were taken to assure the safety of Alar?

A: Agrochemicals, such as Alar, are subject to continuous review and, if new evidence emerges, their use is re-evaluated. The Government Regulatory Agencies must consider the health of the people using the chemical, who are likely to be exposed to higher levels than the normal consumer. If an agrochemical is reviewed it is not necessarily an indication that there is a proven hazard. The review process is ongoing and will review all agrochemicals over time. If there is any doubt an agrochemical is reviewed immediately.

Q: Does Alar cause Cancer?

A: The evidence is not clear cut but at very high dose levels there is some indication that it causes tumours in mice. The high doses in laboratory feeding trials are several million times more than the level of human exposure to Alar. The type of tumour found in the mice are very rare in humans. ✳

Q: Is Alar considered safe for use?

A: The Independent Advisory Committee on Pesticides concluded that there was no risk to health from Alar if used under approved conditions. Even if adults ate up to 30,000 treated apples a day and infants consumed 400 jars of apple dessert over the same period they would still be within the Acceptable Daily Intake recommended for Alar.

Q: Can Alar still be present in small amounts?

A: Alar has not been used to spray British orchards for a number of years, but very low levels of Alar residue were found in some trees shortly after spraying stopped. This was due to the fact that Alar is systemic which means that once it is applied to a tree it is taken up by the whole plant.

For this reason British apples were monitored for residual levels of Alar up until 1991. A decreasing amount of residue was found each year and in 1991 only two samples were found to contain Alar, one of cooking apples and another sample of dessert apples. The detected levels in both cases fell well within the proposed Maximum Residue Limit (MRL). The amounts found were not a risk to health.

TECNAZENE

Q: What is Tecnazene?

A: Tecnazene is a fine white powder which is applied to potatoes during long-term storage. The purpose of the powder is to prevent potatoes from sprouting. The amount applied is regulated by strict Government legislation.

Q: Does Tecnazene cause cancer in rats?

A: There is some evidence that rats given Tecnazene at very high levels in the diet have contracted cancer, but the results to date are inconclusive.

Q: Is it true that residues of Tecnazene have been reported to be above the safe level?

A: In a recent survey of 256 samples of potatoes analysed after washing, only one sample was slightly above the advisory Maximum Residue Limit(MRL) for Tecnazene (The MRL for Tecnazene is 5.0ppm, the sample contained 5.5ppm). These data indicate that even consumers absorbing a diet heavily dependent on potatoes are unlikely to exceed the Acceptable Daily Intake (ADI) for Tecnazene. See page VIII-3 for explanations of ADI and MRL.

Q: Are new potatoes safer to eat than old potatoes?

A: Tecnazene is not present in new potatoes because they are not stored for long periods so treatment is unnecessary. Old potatoes are stored and therefore treatment to prevent sprouting is required. Levels are usually higher just after application of the Tecnazene but these generally fall over time.

Q: Is it safe to eat jacket potatoes?

A: The levels of Tecnazene and other sprout inhibitors on potatoes will be low. A further reduction in the level will occur during cooking as up to 80% of the Tecnazene will be broken down.

It is also recommended that potatoes should be thoroughly washed before cooking. The MRL's permitted for potatoes will take into consideration the whole potato - hence the peel is included.

Q: How can you tell if Tecnazene has been used on potatoes?

A: The potato will show no visible signs of being treated. However, any potatoes labelled organic will not have been treated.

Q: Are there alternatives to using Tecnazene?

A: Increasingly the compound, Chlorpropham, is replacing Tecnazene as a sprouting inhibitor.

GENETIC ENGINEERING

What do a new vaccine against rabies, tomatoes that last longer on the shelf and cows that produce more milk have in common? Very little you might think! In fact, these and many more 'designed' microbes, plants and animals are all the products of modern genetic engineering.

What is genetic engineering?

Put simply, it is a modern, more precise form of selective breeding - a procedure practised and accepted by man for centuries. Indeed for so long, we rarely give it a thought. Few of us pause to think how the many varieties of certain garden plants, the cereal crops, and the farm and domestic animals that we know today came into being. Some are very different from those our ancestors would have known because they have been developed by selective breeding.

For example, let us think about our pet animals. Any dog you care to name from, the Doberman to the tiny Chihuahua, is with us because of this kind of genetic engineering. Dogs have been interbred from the Wolf since the first breeders selected and mated a Wolf dog and a bitch, one or both of which had certain desirable characteristics - characteristics that made them more obedient, docile or more attractive to look at. Their off-spring, by further selection and mating, eventually became the dog breeds we know today.

There are many other examples - the vast variety of roses in our gardens have been produced in much the same way. Plant breeders are still trying to produce the perfect blue rose! The same applies to modern strains of wheat and to the yeasts used in brewing and baking. Indeed without these largely desirable changes, engineered by selective breeding, both our food and our environment would be much poorer and duller. Sometimes these changes have happened by chance. It is quite likely that the plant that gave rise to our present sweetcorn came about by the chance interbreeding of two quite ordinary grasses and was then cultivated by man.

These age-old methods are time-consuming, costly and very 'hit and miss'. The desired new form of plant or animal may not arise or may not be detectable immediately in the off-spring. Further, during interbreeding for a desired characteristic, undesirable characteristics can also appear; a larger, more luscious looking tomato is of little use if the taste is not good or it is more likely to become mouldy.

So when scientists discovered precisely how characteristics are passed on from one generation to the next, they devised ways of speeding up the process and making it more exact - the technique referred to as genetic engineering.

How is it done?

Sometime ago scientists found that the information that determines the characteristics of all living organisms, from microbes to man, is contained in a complex chemical material called deoxyribonucleic acid (DNA). This material is present in all living cells and is passed on from generation to generation in the egg, pollen or sperm.

The structure of DNA is that of a double helix (a spiral curve like a corkscrew) - two long strands helically bound together. Each strand is made up of four chemicals, called bases: adenine (A), guanine (G), thymine (T) and cytosine (C), held together in a sugar-phosphate background. The two strands are held together by pairing between these bases; A always pairs with T, and G with C.

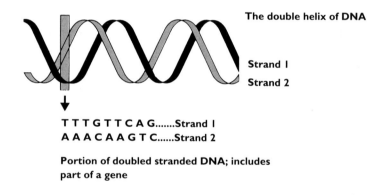

The double helix of DNA

Strand I

Strand 2

T T T G T T C A G.......Strand I
A A A C A A G T C......Strand 2

Portion of doubled stranded DNA; includes part of a gene

Segments of the DNA, called genes, contain the information that determines the inherited characters of individuals. All genes contain the bases A, G, C, T - it is the sequence of these bases in the gene that determines its particular information. Some small genes contain only a hundred bases, others many thousands. Genes can, therefore, be regarded as individual beads in a string of DNA. These strings, called chromosomes, are composed of many thousands of genes each containing the information that together determines the characteristics of all living things. Bacteria contain only one chromosome but animals and plants contain a number.

Genetic engineering has been made possible by three main developments in the last 20 to 30 years. First, scientists developed methods to physically detect the position of individual genes on the DNA of the chromosome. Then substances, called restriction endonucleases, were discovered. These substances, 'scissor enzymes', have the ability to cut the double-stranded DNA at specific locations so that individual genes or parts of genes can be 'cut out' of the chromosome.

cut   cut

...... T C C \ G A T T T A A \ A .....

. . .   .

AGG   CTAAATT   T

Next, scientists discovered other enzymes, called ligases. These have the ability to 'paste together' genes from the same or different living organisms.

By using these procedures of 'snip' and 'paste', genes, or parts of them, can be transferred from one organism to another. In this way individual desirable characteristics can be transferred or undesirable ones deleted. The 'new' characteristics are passed on in the recipient individual from generation to generation. This accomplishes in one generation what, in the past took plant and animal breeders many generations to achieve. Further, genetic engineering allows the transfer of genes (though as yet to a very limited extent) between different kinds of organisms - animals, plants and microbes.

An example is the transfer of the gene responsible for the production of rennet (chymosin) in calves' stomachs to a yeast; (see diagram below)

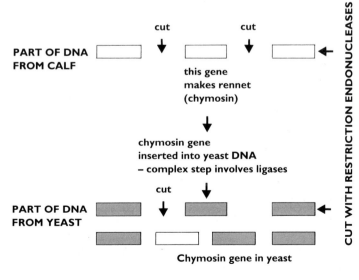

YEAST PRODUCES CHYMOSIN

Why do it?

Partly to understand more about life. Increasingly, however, genetic engineering is being used to serve man in a variety of ways. These include the faster, more efficient and predictable development of products for use in medicine, agriculture, waste management and pollution control. The technique is also beginning to offer real hope in the prevention of conditions such as cystic fibrosis.

The benefits of genetic engineering are potentially very great. Potentially, because despite the publicity, some positive and some alarmist, the technology is still in its infancy. Many technical problems have to be solved and ethical considerations debated before the full potential of genetic engineering can be realised in practice. Much of the current discussion concerns what might be, rather than what it is.

What are the benefits?

As perceived by responsible practitioners, the benefits that can accrue from genetically engineered or 'designed' genes include:
▷ Cost effective production of drugs and enzymes currently in short supply - some of these are already marketed or awaiting marketing.
▷ Plants that:
are able to utilise atmospheric nitrogen rather than having to be fed on environmentally damaging nitrate fertilisers;
are resistant to various diseases;
have a higher crop yield, or produce crops with different flavours, or are themselves more resistant to deterioration when stored.
▷ Animals that:
are free from at least some inherited disabilities - and this includes man;
produce more milk, better meat for consumption, wool or hide with improved quality.

The farm, factory and our food.

Many of the potential and actual achievements listed above have implications for our food - at the farm and the factory and at the point of sale.

Examples of genetic engineering that are, or soon may be, used in food production include:
▷ The introduction of 'resistance' into plants to counteract herbicides and the diseases caused by insects and microbes.

▷ Sugar beet resistant to the herbicide, glyphosphate, has the advantage of not being damaged when fields are sprayed to kill weeds.

▷ Other plants have been made toxic to caterpillars by introducing genes from a bacterium that makes a caterpillar toxin.

▷ Potatoes have been given resistance to a virus that causes leaf roll, a major disease of this crop.

None of these has yet been exploited commercially, though trials have taken place.

▷ Some bacteria that live on plants potentiate frost damage. The gene component responsible for this has been deleted from these bacteria to produce 'ice-minus' mutants. These 'ice-minus' bacteria when sprayed on crops displace the natural bacterial population and reduce frost damage. These have been tested on strawberry, citrus plants and potato plants under strictly controlled conditions in the USA.

▷ Tomatoes that do not soften rapidly on ripening have been produced by genetic techniques that turn off the gene that produces the softening enzyme. Such tomatoes remain firm during transport and are therefore less likely to be attacked by mould. Also, the 'non-squishy' tomatoes can be plucked when ripe, thus retaining a better flavour to the point of sale. Such tomatoes are now being tested but have not yet been approved for sale in shops.

▷ Milk production in cows has been increased by the injection of a hormone called bovine somatotrophin (BST). This hormone is produced naturally produced in cows. By genetic engineering, the BST gene has been transferred to a bacterium. This has enabled relatively large amounts of BST to be produced in the laboratory and the purified material injected into cows to increase milk yields significantly. However, trials have shown that some cows treated with high doses of BST (higher than those required to increase milk yields) may be more prone to illness.

▷ An important stage in cheese production is the curdling of milk. From time immemorial this has been achieved by a substance called rennet, extracted from the stomach lining of calves. However, the genetic material responsible for the production of the curdling enzyme, chymosin, in calf rennet can now be transferred to yeast cells. Since the beginning of 1991, chymosin, produced by yeasts, has been available for the production of cheese sold in this country. All the evidence indicates this is a safe product, more reliable and cheaper than calf rennet. The cheese is also more acceptable to vegetarians.

▷ A baker's yeast genetically modified to produce better raising in bread is now available for use in this country.

What are the concerns?

That there are concerns, both scientific and ethical, about the possible dangers of genetic engineering is understandable. Scientists and Governments are highly aware of these problems.

Indeed, it was scientists themselves in the USA in the 1970s that called for a complete ban on research involving genetic engineering until more was known about the possible consequences. As a result, various regulatory bodies have been set up by Governments in many countries, including the UK.

Scientific questions are:

▷ 'Will plants genetically engineered to produce desirable characteristics also prove to be uncontrollable weeds?' - and, more importantly, 'will genetically engineered bacteria cause unforeseen problems if they are deliberately or accidentally released into the environment?'

There is no evidence from the trials carried out so far that either of these possibilities is likely. Indeed, it is known that the 'ice-minus' bacterium used to control frost damage to plants does not survive in the environment as well as its 'parent'.

▷ 'Will the laboratory-transferred genes stay the same once they are introduced into other organisms?'

▷ 'What will be the consequences if the transferred gene develops an ability to transfer itself into another organism - like a virus does when it infects - and is 'integrated' by natural means into other organisms?'

It is questions like these that have prompted Governments to introduce strict controls on scientific work that involves genetic engineering.

▷ 'What are the dangers associated with using drugs, hormones and enzymes produced by genetically engineered organisms?'

Here the problems, though not trivial, are not so great because all these products are completely separated from the organisms that produce them. They are tested in the same way as all other new materials used in medicines and foods. The problems detected in using high doses of BST could only have been found after controlled trials.

Ethical questions - those that relate to whether we ought to carry out such work at all - are more difficult to answer.

▷ 'Have we the right to interfere with Nature?'

This question is a little late. Man has been manipulating Nature since the earliest times. Selective breeding of plants and animals has been accepted for centuries.

▷ 'Yes, but genetic engineering makes possible the transfer of genes from man to bacteria, or bacteria to plants - is this unacceptable interference?'

There is no ready answer. Modern science has made these transfers possible. Whether we exploit the technology, and, if so, how far we exploit it, is a matter for informed public debate. Such a debate will touch on deeply held beliefs as well as scientific facts and commercial considerations.

What are the safeguards?

In the UK all work involving genetic engineering, whether carried out in university or industrial laboratories, has to meet criteria set out by the Advisory Committee on Genetic Manipulation (ACGM), an agency of the Health and Safety Executive (HSE). Once produced, genetically engineered products for use in medicine or food are assessed by other bodies.

In the case of food or food additives, these are assessed by:

▷ The Food Advisory Committee (FAC) - which is intended to be an independent body of experts not representing any particular interests.

▷ The Committee on Toxicity of Chemicals in Food, Consumer Products and the Environment (COT), whose members are appointed by the Chief Medical Officer.

▷ The Advisory Committee on Novel Foods and Processes (ACNFP) - another body of experts which is intended to be independent.

The role of these bodies is twofold: to ensure that safety in genetic engineering is maintained and also to ensure that it is seen to be maintained.

What is important is that all information is made available to everyone in as clear a form as possible as soon as it is practicable to do so. Then the benefits and risks of all new applications of genetic engineering can be discussed openly by scientists, regulatory bodies and the public.

FOOD AND HEALTH

Q: What are sugars?

A: Sugar is often assumed to be merely the sweet, white granular substance we add to drinks and food. However, sugar (sucrose) is just one of the large family of available carbohydrates, and is refined from sugar beet or sugar cane.
Other sugars include:
1. Glucose which is found in grapes and in small amounts in other foods.
2. Fructose, or fruit sugar which is found in fruits and honey.
3. Lactose or milk sugar makes milk sweet and produces the caramel flavour you taste in cooked milk.
   Dextrose, (an alternative name for glucose) maltose and corn syrup are also used as sweeteners.

Q: Is one sugar better for you than another?

A: No. All sugars are similar in the respect that, apart from the energy they provide, they have very little nutritional value. Some people are intolerant of specific sugars for example lactose intolerant. If you are medically intolerant of a sugar, avoid it. All sugars contain the same number of calories.

Q: Are artificial sweeteners sugars?

A: No. Artificial sweeteners are not sugars. Some are produced specifically to provide a sweet taste without providing calories, for example, Aspartame and Saccharin. Both are used in such small quantities that they add virtually no calories to the food. Other artificial sweeteners do provide energy in the form of calories, for example, Sorbitol which may be used in drinks for diabetics.

Q: What is cholesterol?

A: Cholesterol is a fat-like substance which is produced in the bodies of animals and humans and it forms part of the complicated structure that makes up the cell membrane. As a result it will therefore be naturally found in animal foods such as cheese, egg yolk, shellfish, liver and kidney. It may also be found in much smaller quantities in vegetable foods.

Q: Since I understand that the body produces cholesterol naturally, why does it matter if I eat food high in cholesterol?

A: There is currently much debate about cholesterol and it seems that eating food that is high in cholesterol may not be the main issue.

It is recommended that those people who are concerned about their cholesterol level should avoid foods that are particularly high in cholesterol, such as liver, eggs and shellfish. However, this is to some extent overshadowed by the wider issue of reducing total fat intake in the diet and in particular reducing the proportion of saturated fats in the diet, which are believed to be partly responsible for the formation of cholesterol in the body.

Q: What is hydrogenated vegetable oil?

A: Hydrogenation is the term used to describe the method by which liquid oil can be hardened to form solid fats such as margarine.

The process converts some of the unsaturated fat to saturated fat, which makes the fat harder. The more hydrogenated the oil the harder the margarine produced and the more saturated the fat will become. The resulting fat has a higher melting point. Various degrees of hydrogenation are used to produce specific physical characteristics for example soft or hard margarine

Q: If margarine is hydrogenated does this mean it is no longer polyunsaturated?

A: On average 65% of the fatty acids - the units that make up fats - in vegetable oil are polyunsaturated. Hardening of the oil (hydrogenation) into margarine will convert between 10% and 15% of the polyunsaturated fatty acids to saturated fatty acids to give a spreadable margarine. If the claim 'high in polyunsaturates' is made then at least 45% of the fat is polyunsaturated. Hard or block margarine will contain less than 10% polyunsaturates.

Q: Is it true that hydrogenation produces unusual fatty acids?

A: Yes. A proportion of the fatty acids produced during the process belong to a group known as trans-fatty acids. Trans-fatty acids are unusually shaped and there is some evidence that trans-monounsaturated fatty acids may increase the blood cholesterol. Because trans-fatty acids behave in a similar way to saturated fatty acids they are often included with saturated fatty acids for nutrition tables.

Q: Which vegetable oil is best to use when frying? Can fat change when cooking?

A: The choice depends on personal preference for the individual flavours of the oil. Deep frying will change the nature of the oil over a period of time. This is due to gradual oxidation (the early stages of rancidity) which will subsequently have an adverse effect on the flavour and taste of the oil. This is recognised by three main changes:
1. The oil becomes dark in colour.
2. The oil will foam on the surface when food is added.
3. Flavours may be transferred from one food to another.

CARE OF OIL WHEN DEEP FRYING.

The following points should be followed:
1. Depending on food items to be fried, use oil no more than 6 or 7 times then discard.
2. Dispose of the oil as soon as any of the earlier mentioned changes occur.
3. After use allow oil to cool and always filter oil into a clean storage container.
4. Never top-up oil with fresh oil, dispose of old oil and start again with fresh oil.
These recommendations also apply to frying in fat. Although frying in oil is probably healthier than frying in fat you would be best advised to choose an alternative cooking method if you are concerned about your total fat intake (see chapter II for cooking methods).

Q: Is a diet high in olive oil good for you?

A: The UK has one of the highest incidence of heart disease in the world and this is thought to be linked in part to our diet which is high in saturated fat. Mediterranean countries have a lower incidence of heart disease and this phenomenon has been partly attributed to the fact that in Mediterranean countries a greater proportion of polyunsaturated or monounsaturated fats are eaten in the form of olive oil and vegetable oils, and a lower proportion of hard saturated fats such as butter and lard are eaten.

Some individuals therefore may well benefit from eating a Mediterranean style diet that is high in olive oil and other unsaturated vegetable oils but low in saturated fats providing they are eating sufficient of the other dietary components (see chapter XII).

The World Health Organisation recommends that the total amount of fat in our diet should provide between 15% and 30% of the energy (calories) we require. On average in the UK we currently obtain around 42% of our energy from fat, so most of us would be best advised to reduce our fat intake. The World Health

Organisation also recommends that we should maximise our intake of bread, cereals and potatoes to obtain 50-70% of our energy from these products. In addition an intake of at least 400g of fruit, vegetables and salad including 30g of pulses per day is advisable.

COFFEE

Q: Is drinking coffee bad for you?

A: No. In moderation coffee is not bad for a healthy adult.

Q: Does drinking coffee increase the risk of heart disease?

A: It is generally accepted that the origins of heart disease are multifaceted. Factors including heredity, lifestyle, smoking are all believed to have an influence. While diet is undoubtedly important it would be foolish to pin point any one food as the causative factor of heart disease in any particular individual.

Reports of an isolated Norwegian study, that implied that drinking an excess of 'stewed' or 'boiled' coffee may increase the risk of heart disease, were based on results that found that those with the greatest tendency towards heart disease drank more than nine cups of 'stewed' coffee a day. Studies carried out elsewhere have not shown such an association.

'Stewed' or 'boiled' coffee is prepared by boiling coffee grounds in an open pan, this is quite different from percolating coffee. If you filter or percolate your coffee as opposed to boiling it, or if you use instant coffee, you need not concern yourself as this is unlikely to affect an overall tendency towards heart disease.

Q: Is there any truth in the rumour that excessive drinking of coffee during pregnancy can lead to the child developing diabetes?

A: No. The reason the connection has been made is that studies have shown that certain countries which had high coffee consumption also had a high incidence of diabetes but the two are not connected. As part of a balanced diet moderate coffee drinking is not a threat to health of either the mother or the unborn child.

Q: Is the caffeine in coffee bad for you?

A: Some people are more sensitive to caffeine than others. If you are sensitive to caffeine it may make you tense, over excited or irritable and may lead to sleepless nights.

Q: What is caffeine?

A: Caffeine is an odourless, slightly bitter substance that is naturally present in a variety of plants including tea, coffee and cocoa.

Q: What are the effects of caffeine on the body?

A: Caffeine is a stimulant, and it makes you feel more awake. Its properties have been known for centuries and it is commonly used in medicines and carbonated drinks.

Q: How is coffee decaffeinated?

A: There are two methods.
1. The first is known as the natural decaffeination method. Before the beans are roasted:
a) Pure water is converted to steam and sprayed over the coffee beans.
b) Carbon dioxide (the gas that makes soda water fizzy) bubbles around the beans and gently removes the caffeine which dissolves in the water.
c) Finally, the beans are dried by warm air. The beans are ready to be roasted and processed in the normal way.

2. The second method uses a solvent called methylene chloride to extract the caffeine. A tiny residue of the solvent is left behind after decaffeination although it is further reduced when the coffee is actually made.

Q: Is it true that methylene chloride causes cancer?

A: Studies in the USA indicated that at very high doses methylene chloride produced tumours in rats. However, a human would have to drink 10,000 cups of coffee a day to consume the equivalent quantity of methylene chloride given to the rats in the study. Methylene chloride at the levels found in decaffeinated coffee is considered safe.

ALL YOU NEED TO KNOW ABOUT NUTRITION

'You are what you eat' goes the age old saying, so a good diet with plenty of nutritious food should go some way to keeping you healthy. But what is 'a good diet' and how can you recognise 'nutritious food'?

Newspapers, magazines, television and radio are full of advice about food but in order to make sense of this deluge of dietary information you need to understand some basic nutritional facts. Certain substances are essential to human beings if our bodies are to grow and function in the normal way. These 'essential nutrients' are:

---

supply of energy from
carbohydrates
fat
protein,

---

fats
(which include essential fatty acids)

---

protein

---

vitamins

---

minerals

---

others
(such as oxygen and water)

A prolonged deficiency or excess of any one of these nutrients in your diet could lead to health problems, so it is important to know not only what kinds of food you need to eat, but also whether you are eating too much or not enough of any particular nutrient. If you are trying to plan a healthy diet, think about the kinds of food you eat and the amounts of different foodstuffs relative to one another. For example, it is fine to consume a lot of bread and relatively little salt as part of your diet, but eating vast amounts of cream and hardly any vegetables would not be a good idea.

Think of a healthy diet as something you build in a pyramid shape (see diagram overleaf); the bottom layer contains foods you can eat in large quantities, the middle layer things that should be taken in moderation, and the top layer foods you should only eat a little of. If you have a broad range of foods and stick to the proportions suggested in the pyramid, your diet will be healthy and nutritious.

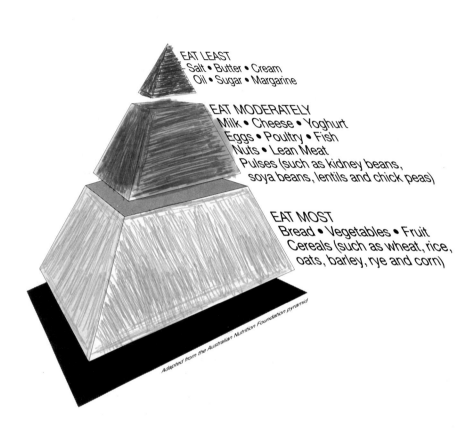

EAT LEAST
Salt • Butter • Cream
Oil • Sugar • Margarine

EAT MODERATELY
Milk • Cheese • Yoghurt
Eggs • Poultry • Fish
Nuts • Lean Meat
Pulses (such as kidney beans,
soya beans, lentils and chick peas)

EAT MOST
Bread • Vegetables • Fruit
Cereals (such as wheat, rice,
oats, barley, rye and corn)

Adapted from the Australian Nutrition Foundation pyramid

Let us look at the essential nutrients in more detail;

CARBOHYDRATES (starches, sugars and fibre)

Carbohydrates provide a large proportion of the calories or energy in our diet.
There are two main types: simple carbohydrates, such as glucose and sucrose,
which are commonly referred to as sugars, and complex carbohydrates. Some
complex carbohydrates are digestible, like starch, while others are indigestible
and form the 'fibre' in food.

All carbohydrates are useful to the body but it is important to get the balance
right between the different kinds of carbohydrate. In the last 150 years or so,
people have begun to consume more and more refined foods, especially sucrose
(table sugar), while the proportion of fibre, in the Western diet at least, has fallen.

Q: Why is eating too much sugar a problem?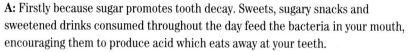

A: Firstly because sugar promotes tooth decay. Sweets, sugary snacks and sweetened drinks consumed throughout the day feed the bacteria in your mouth, encouraging them to produce acid which eats away at your teeth.

And secondly, eating more food than we need provides us with too many calories and can lead us to being overweight. Sweet/sugary foods taste nice and because they do not fill us up can easily be overeaten.

Refined sugar provides 'empty' calories - that is, calories with no other nutrients, so although boiled sweets give your body a quick energy boost, they do not provide any vitamins, minerals, protein or fibre. It is much better to get your carbohydrate from starchy, high-fibre foods which are both filling (so helping to keep your calorie intake down if you are trying to lose weight) and nutritious.

Q: What is so good about fibre?

A: It helps prevent constipation and may protect against other bowel problems including diverticulitis (inflammation of small pouches which protrude from the wall of the intestines in some people) and cancer of the bowel. High-fibre foods can help people lose weight because they are filling and relatively low in calories.

A good intake of fibre every day may also improve the blood sugar control in people who have diabetes. Some people believe that soluble fibre (which is found in oats, beans and apples, as well as many other fruits and vegetables) helps to lower blood cholesterol levels.

Therefore, increasing the amount of fibre in your diet is generally a wise step to take, but that does not mean scattering spoonfuls of unpalatable bran over your cornflakes or your favourite pudding! Instead, it is much better to eat some kind of fibre-rich food at every meal; the choice is huge - fruit (fresh and dried), vegetables (peas, sweetcorn, spinach and potatoes with their skins on are particularly good), wholemeal bread or soft grain white breads, pulses (such as lentils, chick peas, baked beans and various kinds of bean), brown rice, wholemeal pasta, and high-fibre breakfast cereals.

FATS

There are basically two types of fats: saturated and unsaturated. Fats naturally contain a mixture of these. Saturated fats are found predominantly in fat associated with meat (especially beef, lamb and pork), in suet, lard and dripping, in dairy products such as milk, cheese and butter, and in some vegetable oils, for example coconut and palm oil. They are 'hidden' in many biscuits, cakes, sauces and puddings. Unsaturated fats can be split into two categories namely monounsaturated and polyunsaturated. Polyunsaturated are the more common of the two. Unsaturated fats are found in oily fish such as herring, mackerel and trout, in nuts, sunflower, corn and soya oils, and in soft margarines that are labelled 'high in polyunsaturates'.

Q: Is all fat bad for you?

A: No. Fat is another source of energy in our diet, and certain fats are needed to help make and repair body cells. But most of us eat too much fat, and would be well advised to reduce our intake of saturated fats. That is because eating a lot of saturated fats may raise the level of cholesterol in your blood, and the cholesterol may then 'fur up' your arteries, impairing the bloodflow to your heart and increasing your risk of a future heart attack. A high fat intake in the diet can also make you overweight and may be linked to certain types of cancer.

There are several ways to decrease total fat, and increase the proportion of polyunsaturated and monounsaturated fats in your diet.

▷ Do not fry food - grill, bake, boil, poach, steam or roast it whenever possible.
▷ Increase your intake of fruit and vegetables.
▷ Increase your intake of wholegrain cereals.
▷ If you do use oil or fat for cooking, use as little as possible and choose one that is low in saturated fat and high in polyunsaturates or monounsaturates. Sunflower, soya, olive and corn oil are the best.
▷ Use kitchen paper or a spoon to remove the fat that comes to the surface of casseroles, stews and gravy. Drain off the fat from mince and curries.
▷ Use skimmed or semi-skimmed milk instead of full-fat milk.
▷ Spread fat thinly on bread. Rather than using butter, hard margarine or ordinary soft margarine, choose a low fat spread or a margarine that is high in poly-unsaturates.
▷ Use high fat cheese sparingly. Have cottage cheese or reduced-fat cheeses instead of higher-fat cheeses such as ordinary Cheddar, Stilton, and Camembert.
▷ Use low fat yoghurt instead of cream on fruit and in savoury dishes, and instead of mayonnaise and salad dressings.
▷ Cut down on cakes, biscuits, crisps, chocolate and chips.

PROTEINS

Our bodies need protein in all cells and to help form muscle, bone, connective tissue and certain hormones. The amount of protein you need every day depends on your body size, rate of growth and the presence or absence of disease. Amino acids are the building blocks from which proteins are made; some cannot be formed in the body but are required for normal health so they are termed 'essential' amino acids.

Protein is sometimes ranked according to the quantity of essential amino acids it contains. High quality protein (such as that in meat, eggs and dairy products and soya beans) contains significant amounts of all the essential amino acids. Lower quality protein contains all of the essential amino acids, but not in adequate amounts. Vegetable proteins are generally of lower quality than animal ones, but certain combinations, or cereals and pulses will provide all the essential amino acids. A wide ranging and balanced vegetarian diet can therefore be just as good a source of proteins as one containing meat.

Q: Can you have too much, or too little, protein in your diet?

A: Most of us get plenty of protein in our diet and, in the West at least, protein deficiency is very rare. For healthy people, excess protein in the diet causes no harm. If you consume more protein than you need, it is simply broken down and excreted from your body. However, a few people, for example those suffering from kidney or liver failure, may need to restrict their protein intake.

VITAMINS

Vitamins are necessary for health and growth, but it is difficult to say exactly how much of each vitamin any individual needs per day. Women who are pregnant or breastfeeding, for example, often need a higher intake of vitamins than other adults, and vitamin requirements may alter when people are ill. Although babies and children obviously have much smaller bodies to maintain than adults, their requirements for certain vitamins are relatively high because they are growing.

Vitamin supplements have become increasingly popular in recent years, marketed as a treatment for everything from premenstrual tension to leg ulcers. On the principle that if a little of something is good for you, a lot must be even better, some people now take megadoses of vitamins every day. However, overdosing on vitamins can have serious side effects. For example, too much Vitamin A can cause liver and bone damage and large doses of Vitamin C may cause side effects including diarrhoea and kidney stones.

The evidence for benefits from vitamin supplements is far from proven and anyone contemplating taking them must be aware that there are potential dangers in consuming large doses of vitamins.

Vitamin A

There are two types of Vitamin A. Retinol which is found in animal fats such as eggs, milk and butter, and various Vitamin A-type compounds, the most important of which is beta-carotene found in carrots and dark green vegetables. The most concentrated sources of Vitamin A are liver and fish liver oils such as cod liver oil.

Vitamin A makes eyes readily adaptable to light and protects the skin and moist surfaces of the eyes, nose, throat and bronchial tubes from disease.

Lack of Vitamin A can result in dry eyes, night blindness and poor resistance to infections. Beta-carotene may play a role in helping to prevent some types of cancer. However, pregnant women or women who are likely to become pregnant should avoid a high Vitamin A intake as this could harm their unborn baby.

Vitamin B complex

Vitamin B is really a group of at least eleven different substances: Vitamins B1 (thiamine), B2 (riboflavin), B3 (nicotinic acid and nicotinamide), B5 (pantothenic acid), B6 (pyridoxine), B12, folic acid, biotin, choline and inositol. The B group of vitamins is destroyed by prolonged cooking.

The group of vitamins helps to release energy from carbohydrates, protein, alcohol and fats. Deficiency can cause damage to nerves, muscles, the heart and skin, and lack of Vitamin B12 or folic acid may result in anaemia. Toxicity due to overdosing from the B vitamins is rare as they are readily excreted from the body but large doses of Vitamin B6 can lead to numbness and tingling in the hands or feet, due to nerve damage. This is reversible when supplements are stopped. Because of such potential dangers it is best to get professional advice - from your GP or local pharmacist, for example - before taking vitamin supplements.

Good food sources of the B vitamins are brewers' yeast, meat, wholegrain cereals, vegetables, eggs, milk, bread, fortified breakfast cereals, yeast extracts.

Vitamin C

Vitamin C or ascorbic acid is the vitamin most easily lost in the preparation of meals as it is destroyed by exposure to air by solution in cooking water and by anything more than the briefest cooking. Vitamin C is found in most fruits, green vegetables, tomatoes and potatoes. It prevents scurvy, aids wound healing and helps us absorb iron from our food. Moderate supplements of Vitamin C (say 100-200 mg per day) may be useful and safe for certain groups such as the elderly, smokers and alcoholics.

Doses of more than 500 mg per day may also interact with low dose contraceptive pills, bringing about the same risk usually only associated with the 'older' high dosed pills.

Vitamin D

Vitamin D is formed mainly by the action of sunlight on our skin, but it is also found in liver, fish oil, milk, fortified breakfast cereals, butter and margarine. It helps us to form strong bones and healthy teeth. Deficiency of Vitamin D, caused by insufficient exposure to sunlight and/or a poor intake of the vitamin in the diet, may cause rickets (with resulting bone deformities) in children and osteomalacia (softening of the bones) in adults. Too much Vitamin D can raise blood calcium levels excessively, causing nausea, vomiting, headaches, drowsiness, thirst, and eventually kidney failure.

Vitamin E

Good food sources of Vitamin E are nuts, vegetable oils, seeds, soya, eggs and margarine. The major function of Vitamin E is probably to protect our body cells from certain kinds of damage. It may also help to prevent heart disease and cancer. Deficiency of Vitamin E is extremely rare except in premature infants. Toxicity is unusual but anyone taking anticoagulant tablets should not use Vitamin E supplements because this may result in excessive bleeding.

Vitamin K

Vitamin K is necessary for normal blood clotting. Deficiency is extremely rare after the first few months of life. Because young babies may suffer from a lack of Vitamin K, many paediatricians recommend that all newborn infants are given a single dose of the vitamin, usually at birth.

MINERALS

Minerals such as calcium, phosphorus, magnesium, sodium, potassium and chlorine are necessary to normal life. Trace elements including iron, zinc, copper, manganese, iodine, chromium, selenium, molybdenum, cobalt and sulphur are also needed in very small quantities for healthy body metabolism.

Calcium

Calcium is needed for healthy bones and teeth, as well as for blood coagulation and normal nerve and muscle function. A good calcium intake is particularly important during childhood when over 90 per cent of bone tissue is laid down. After the menopause, women are at increased risk of osteoporosis (thinning of the bones) and although the most effective way to prevent, and possibly restore, bone loss is by using hormone replacement therapy (HRT), a high calcium intake may also be of some help. Good food sources are milk (full fat, semi-skimmed or skimmed), cheese, dark green vegetables, pulses, nuts, and sesame seeds.

Iron

Iron is needed for the formation of blood, and deficiency leads to anaemia which can make you feel tired, weak and even breathless. Women who are pregnant, breastfeeding, or who have heavy periods are most at risk of anaemia, as are infants and children because they need extra iron to allow their blood volume and muscle tissue to increase. Good dietary sources of iron include meat, liver, eggs, peas, beans, cocoa, dark green vegetables, dried fruit and fortified breakfast cereals.

> Those in the at-risk groups may need to take iron supplements, but should consult their doctor before doing so.

SALT

We all need some salt (sodium chloride) in our diet but the average daily consumption of salt is at least ten times more than our bodies require.

Surprisingly, perhaps, most of this is not from salt added during cooking or at the table, but instead is found in processed foods. Crisps, salted nuts and snack foods, tinned vegetables, tinned and packet soups, salt beef, smoked mackerel, bacon and gammon all have a relatively high salt content. In susceptible people, salt may contribute to high blood pressure and as there is no way of determining in advance which people are likely to be affected in this way, it is probably a good idea for all of us to try and reduce the amount of salt we eat.

SPECIAL DIETARY NEEDS

The amount of energy and nutrients that we need from our diet varies throughout our lives. Because of these changing requirements it is important to know when you need more (or less) of particular kinds of foods, so you can make the necessary adjustments to your diet.

YOUNG CHILDREN 1 - 5 YEARS

Children's dietary needs are rather different from those of adults. The kind of high fibre, low fat diet which is recommended for most adults is not suitable for young children: too much fibre fills them up without providing sufficient calories, and restricting their fat intake would reduce their daily calorie intake even further. Young children need a lot of dietary energy, or calories, relative to their small size and because they find it difficult to consume large amounts of food at any one time, smaller, more frequent meals, containing a relatively high fat and low fibre content are best for them.

Children are notoriously finicky about food, often refusing everything but their favourite dishes. Ideally, their diet should contain some meat, fish and poultry (or soya products for vegetarian children), milk, eggs, cheese and yoghurt, bread and cereals, vegetables and fruit. Even if their diet seems very narrow and repetitive to you, so long as they are eating most of these kinds of food on a fairly regular basis, they will probably get all the nutrients they need. Remember, snacks between meals provide a good opportunity for increasing a child's food intake; milk, fresh fruit, and sandwiches are preferable to sweets and sugary foods. Skimmed milk is not suitable for children under 5, but from 2 years of age they can be given semi-skimmed milk if their diet is varied and they have a good appetite.

Q: What if they won't eat?

A: Children's appetites fluctuate a great deal too, so do not worry if they seem to be eating too little, or too much, unless it goes on for a long time and is causing them to be persistently under, or over-weight. If a child's diet is nutritionally poor for any length of time, or if they are found to be deficient in any nutrient, vitamin or mineral supplements may be recommended. If you are worried about your child's diet, contact your GP or health visitor; they can refer you to a dietician for detailed advice if necessary.

Severe nutritional deficiencies are now much rarer than say, fifty years ago, but anaemia and rickets still affect some children in this country. Anaemia, due to iron deficiency, is probably more common than previously realised; families who eat a restricted diet (for example, due to low income or cultural/religious customs) are most likely to be affected.

Q: What about food allergies?

A: So-called food 'allergies' have been blamed for a variety of problems in children, including hyperactivity, learning disorders and eczema. Opinions vary on how often food is really the underlying culprit in these problems, but even if you think your child is reacting adversely to some food or other, do not tamper with their diet before seeking advice from your GP. Cutting out certain foods could cause significant nutrient deficiencies and if a child's diet does need to be modified, it should always be done with guidance from a dietician.

PREGNANT AND BREASTFEEDING WOMEN

Women do not need to 'eat for two' during pregnancy. A normal well balanced diet will meet all their energy requirements for the first six months, and an extra 200 kcal per day (that is roughly equivalent to two slices of lightly buttered wholemeal bread, or 3oz of lean meat) in the last three months of pregnancy is all the body needs. However, women who are underweight at the start of pregnancy may need to eat more. Women who are breastfeeding need a higher energy intake than usual because their breastmilk has to supply the growing baby's energy needs. An extra 500 kcal per day should be sufficient.

During pregnancy and breastfeeding, requirements for many vitamins and minerals increase, so it is important for women to eat a broad range of foods to ensure a good supply of all these nutrients. Plenty of fresh fruit and vegetables are essential. Women who have a poor diet, are expecting twins, or are found to be anaemic on a routine blood test, may be prescribed supplements of iron and/or folic acid (one of the B vitamins).

Women who have had a baby with a spina bifida or some other severe abnormality of the nervous system are advised to consume extra folic acid (usually in supplement form) BEFORE conception and during early pregnancy because this reduces their risk of having another similarly affected baby. Good sources of folic acid are green vegetables, eggs, wholemeal bread and nuts, but remember it is a vitamin that is easily destroyed by cooking.

As mentioned in the section on Vitamins, pregnant women should not take Vitamin A supplements, or eat liver (due to its high Vitamin A content) because of the risk of damage to the developing baby.

VEGETARIANS AND VEGANS

A vegetarian diet can be perfectly healthy so long as a wide range of foods are eaten to ensure that no vital nutrients are missing. In fact, many vegetarians consume less saturated fat and more fibre than meat-eaters, reducing their risk of heart disease and bowel problems.

Non-meat eaters must rely on vegetable sources for much of their protein, and should eat certain combinations of food to make sure that their diet contains all the essential amino acids. For example, when a pulse and cereal are eaten together (such as baked beans on toast or lentils and rice) they will provide a good quality protein. Soya products are also an excellent source of protein.

Iron from plant foods is poorly absorbed compared with that from animal foods, so vegetarians need to eat plenty of iron-rich foods. Combining these with foods rich in Vitamin C will increase iron absorption.

Vegans only eat foods which have a plant source so all animal foods, including dairy products, are excluded from their diet. This makes them more prone to deficiencies of iron, calcium, Vitamin D and Vitamin B12. Provided they eat plenty of the non-animal foods that are rich in iron and calcium, they should be able to take in adequate amounts of these minerals. Good sources of iron include peas, beans, dark green vegetables, dried fruit, molasses, fortified breakfast cereals and wholemeal bread; sources of calcium include beans, nuts, sesame seeds, dark green vegetables, and molasses; exposure to sunlight will provide adequate Vitamin D. Avoiding B12 deficiency however is more difficult. The stable foods for a vegan diet - cereals, fruits, nuts, pulses, vegetables and other plant foods - contain virtually no Vitamin B12, so the only way to safeguard against deficiency is to use vegan foods containing added Vitamin B12 or to take B12 supplements.

FOOD PACKAGING SAFETY

TIN CANS

Canning is a very effective way of preserving food. Once the food is sealed in the can and heat treated it will remain sterile provided the can remains intact.

Q: Why use tin for cans?

A: Tin is plated onto the surface of steel in order to prevent the steel from rusting. This process helps preserve the can and extend its life.

Q: Are all cans made from tin plate?

A: No. There are many different food packaging materials available. Soft drink cans and some speciality meal cans are made of aluminium, but the use of aluminium cans for food is less common than the traditional tin can.

Q: Can the tin get into the food?

A: Providing the food has been properly canned, there is little risk of excessive tin getting into the food. Acidic fruit such as grapefruit or tomatoes may absorb more tin than other foods because tin will dissolve in acid. For this reason cans containing fruit are often lacquered on the inside.

Q: Why aren't all tin cans laquered?

A: Foods vary greatly in their composition and specification and therefore the type of can used will vary according to the type of food. For example, foods like pulses, such as peas or beans, or meat do not absorb much tin and so do not need a lacquer between the tin and the food.

Q: Is it safe to leave food in open tin cans?

A: No. Food absorbs tin more easily if oxygen is present. Once the tin is opened and exposed to air, the oxygen in the air can encourage food to absorb the tin. For this reason you should remove any remaining food from open tins and place it in a clean, dry, non-metallic container and store in the 'fridge.

Q: Is lead used in the soldering of tin cans?

A: Lead solders, have in the past, been used to seal tin cans. However changes in canning technology have led to this solder being replaced with lead-free solders or welded side seams and as a result there has been a significant reduction in the lead content of these canned foods.

Q: Do canned foods contain additives?

A: Occasionally, canned foods contain additives, more usually to preserve colour. The canning process itself is an effective preservation process so additional preservatives would be unnecessary.

ALUMINIUM

Aluminium is one of the most abundant naturally occurring elements in the Earth's crust. It occurs naturally in soils and, not surprisingly, is found in many fresh foods such as fruit and vegetables.

Q: Is it safe to cook in aluminum?

A: Yes. Research has shown that the transfer of aluminium from utensils into foodstuffs is negligible except when cooking very acidic foods. It may be prudent therefore to cook very acidic foods, such as stewed fruit, in non-aluminium pans.

Copper pans are also unsuitable for very acidic foods such as tomatoes and citrus fruit because the acid can lead to the copper being absorbed by the food.

Q: Are cartons of orange juice safe to drink? What about the aluminium in the carton?

A: Cartons are made from laminated composite. Each layer of the carton offers a functional property to ensure that the content is safe. Although aluminium forms one layer of the laminate, the orange and the aluminium are separated by a film of plastic. The aluminium cannot dissolve through the plastic.

Q: Is it safe to cook with aluminium foil? Is one side of the foil coated?

A: Yes. It is safe to use aluminium foil for cooking. Although the foil is an alloy containing a small quantity of other minor components, it is almost pure aluminium. It is not coated, but achieves its dull and shiny appearance by a process known as calendering, produced by the use of different types of rollers during manufacture. Either side of the foil may be used when cooking.

Q: Does one side reflect heat more than the other? Should I use one side for slower cooking and one side to speed up cooking?

A: In practical terms there is very little difference. If you are grilling it is probably best to have the shiny side up to reflect back some of the heat. If you are roasting it is preferable to have the dull side on the outside and the shiny side facing the meat so that less heat is reflected away from the joint. The overall difference in cooking times is, however, very small.

Q: How much aluminium should you have in a normal diet?

A: Aluminium is not an essential part of the diet, but everyone naturally absorbs a few thousandths of a gram per day. A sub-committee of the World Health Organisation (WHO) reported that a weekly intake of up to 7mg per Kg body weight would not be cause for concern.

Q: Is fruit juice naturally high in aluminium?

A: Aluminium is naturally present in a number of foods including fruits. Recent reports on the level of aluminium in 'fresh' orange juice and 'reconstituted' whole orange juice were based on a comparison between the amount of aluminium in drinking water and the amount in orange juice. This study was conducted by the Department of Renal Medicine at Southmead General Hospital. Unfortunately, this study did not take into account the regional variation of aluminium concentrations in water. More importantly, the study neglected to compare the data found, with the recent review of the tolerable weekly intake of aluminium.

Q: What is the tolerable weekly intake of aluminium?

A: The Joint World Health Organisation and the Food and Agricultural Organisation Expert Committee on Food Additives have allocated a tolerable weekly intake of seven milligrams per kilogram body weight. Therefore, an average adult of approximately sixty kilograms weight can consume approximately sixty milligrams of aluminium per day when averaged over the week.

Q: How much orange juice can be consumed before too much aluminium is consumed?

A: Assuming all the aluminium consumed comes from orange juice, and taking the median level of aluminium content found by the Department of Renal Medicine at Southmead General Hospital as the basis for the calculations; an adult could consume approximately 360 litres of orange juice per day before exceeding the tolerable weekly intake allocated by the Joint Expert Committee on Food Additives.

Q: What other foods are sources of aluminium?

A: Despite the fact that aluminium is the third most abundant element in the earth's crust, its absorption into crops as they are growing is not very large.

Despite not being an essential dietary element we take in some aluminium from foods such as cereal products. Some crops do take up more aluminium than others. Tea has been indicated as one of the foods that has high levels of aluminium. However, the levels of aluminium in the infusion are much lower than in the dry leaf. Aluminium may also be present in food additives used to prevent powdered products from caking together, for example, raising agents such as slow release baking powders, salt, non-dairy creamers, cocoa powders and icing sugar.

Q: Are we eating too much aluminium?

A: Current estimates of aluminium intake indicate that an adult on a varied diet will be consuming in the order of 6-14 milligrams per day. These estimates fall well within the Joint Expert Committee on Food Additives tolerable weekly intake of approximately sixty milligrams per day for an adult and twenty milligrams per day for a child, based on a five year old child weighing approximately twenty kilograms.

Premature babies and extremely young infants may be exposed to a greater retention of aluminium due to their under developed renal (kidney) system, however these infants will not be consuming 'normal' foods. Advice on suitable infant formulas should be sought from your doctor or health visitor.

Q: How much aluminium is there in water?

A: The European Community has proposed that the maximum limit of aluminium in water should be 0.2 milligrams per litre. At this level aluminium would not cause any health concerns if the water were consumed.

Q: Is it true that aluminium is the cause of Alzheimer's disease?

A: There is no clear causal connection between Alzheimer's Disease and aluminium intake.

Although some studies have suggested that the incidence of Alzheimer's Disease is higher in areas where the concentration of aluminium in drinking water is high, this is not universally true. Further, several studies have shown that abnormal 'tangles' of nerves in the brain contain unusually high levels of aluminium, but this is not simply related to dietary exposure.

If the intake of high levels of aluminium was the cause of Alzheimer's Disease, doctors would expect to find a greater percentage of people with the disease in areas of the country with high levels of aluminium in the water, or amongst those with certain medical complaints which require aluminium in the preparation of their drugs. This is not the case and it has been suggested that certain people are genetically more susceptible to aluminium accumulation.

Q: Is it true that soya milk is high in aluminium?

A: Soya milk contains about 10 times more aluminium than cow's milk, which is itself about 10 times higher than human milk.

Babies should only be fed soya milk formulas under medical supervision, or after consultation with the family doctor or nutritionist. If the soya milk formula is correctly reconstituted and the manufacturer's instructions are closely followed, it poses no threat to the health of children. However, babies with kidney problems or those who are premature should only be fed soya milk formulas on medical advice. Baby formulas from cow's milk are considered safe for normal healthy full term infants.

CLING FILM WRAPPINGS AND PLASTIC CONTAINERS

Q: Are cling film wrappings safe?

A: Yes. All food wrappings sold in this country must comply with Government Food Regulations. These Regulations state that food wrappings must neither be hazardous to human health nor bring about a deterioration in the organoleptic characteristics of food (those which stimulate the senses such as taste and smell) or cause an unacceptable change in its natural substance or quality.

Different food types have different properties and for this reason some wrappings are more suitable for some foods than others.

Q: What foods are unsuitable for wrapping and storing in cling film?

A: Cling film should not be used as a wrapping for fatty foods such as cheese, butter, cooked and raw meat with a high proportion of surface fat. However, it is important to remember that food needs to be wrapped to prevent contamination from micro-organisms and dirt such as dust. The dangers from microbial contamination far outweigh any potential danger from the plastic. To wrap fatty foods use a more suitable wrapping, for example a non-plasticised polyethylene film or greaseproof paper. Check the recommended uses indicated on the pack.

Q: What can cling film be used for?

A: Cling film is a very useful wrapping and suitable for most food uses especially covering bowls or containers.

Cling film is not suitable for cooking in conventional ovens and should not come into direct contact with food being cooked in a microwave oven. It can be used to cover food that is defrosting or is being reheated in a microwave oven or to cover containers of food that are being cooked in a microwave oven. The film and the food should not come into direct contact.

Q: Why are fatty and hot cooked foods unsuitable for wrapping in cling film?

A: Some plastics contain components that can migrate into food. One group of components are called plasticisers, which are responsible for producing the flexible clingy property of cling film. The Ministry of Agriculture, Fisheries and Food has expressed concern about the lack of information available concerning some of these plasticisers. The amount of these components migrating into food is normally minute, but transmission will be increased at higher temperatures.

UNTIL FURTHER INFORMATION IS AVAILABLE CLING FILMS SHOULD NOT BE USED TO WRAP AND STORE FATTY FOODS.

Q: Is one type of cling film better than another?

A: There are several different types of plastic wrapping. The more flexible and sticky the wrapping the more likely it is to be highly plasticised. Highly plasticised cling films are more suitable for wrapping and covering containers as they form a good seal. The thicker, less flexible plastics are more suitable for wrapping food as they contain less plasticiser. Foods such as fruit are suitable to wrap in cling film but ensure that any fatty food such as cheese filling in a sandwich is completely covered by the bread and does not come into direct contact with the film.

Q: What alternatives can be used to wrap fatty foods?

A There are a great many alternative food wrappings available. Foods such as cheese can safely be wrapped in greaseproof paper and stored in a plastic container such as a sandwich box. Alternatively, fatty foods can be stored in glass or ceramic bowls with a plate or lid on top. Food should always be covered when stored in a 'fridge.

Q: Is it safe to cook in plastic containers?

A: Food such as boil-in-the-bag meals, microwave TV dinners and steam puddings that are packaged in their own container will be safe, as the container will comply with Government Food Regulations. These plastics are designed for use in hot conditions. Always follow the manufacturer's instructions.

Do not cook in a plastic container which is not designed for that purpose. Ice cream containers and plastic mixing bowls are not suitable cooking utensils.

Q: Is it safe to use cling film or plastic containers in microwave ovens?

A: If you wish to use cling film wrapping, check the instructions for use to establish that it is recommended for use in microwave ovens. If it does not state that it is suitable, do not assume that it is since not all films or plastic containers are suitable for use in a microwave oven. Some may melt and others may cause the migration of plasticisers into the food. If you are not sure whether the film or container is suitable, do not use it. If you have bought a container specifically designed for use in a microwave oven, it should be safe.

HOW THE LAW PROTECTS YOU

HOW THE LAW PROTECTS YOU

The Food Safety Act came into force in January 1991 and replaced the previous Food Act of 1984.

Over the years, food legislation has become more complex in order to ensure the safety of food supplies. The Food Safety Act 1990 is an attempt both to simplify the legislation while ensuring provision is made to cover new areas, and new developments within the food industry. The Act also makes provision for the adoption of European Food Law.

Q: What does the Act cover?

A: The Food Safety Act covers the whole food chain from the farm to the shop. It is also important that the consumer takes the necessary precautions to ensure the safety of the food in the home (see chapter II and IV).

Food sources such as live animals and growing crops, will come under the control of the Act and so the application of veterinary medicines and pesticides will be strictly controlled under the Act.

The Act also requires the registration of food premises, so anyone preparing food for sale will be under its control, not just large manufacturers, or retailers, or restaurants, but also small businesses producing home-made pies or sandwiches.

Q: Who ensures that food law is enforced?

A: In Britain there are two groups of enforcement officers, the Environmental Health Officers (EHO's) who cover public health matters such as the hygiene of food premises and food safety, and the Trading Standards Officers (TSO's) who cover commercial law such as weights and measures and the correct labelling of food products.

Q: What should you do if you buy a defective food product? Who is responsible?

A: If you buy an item which is defective you have three courses of action.
1. Return the item to the seller.
2. Return the item to the manufacturer (the manufacturer's address should be given on the label), who may also be the retailer.
3. Report the matter to your local council's EHO or TSO as appropriate.
4. Take the matter up (via a solicitor) to seek compensation for the defective good(s).

The person responsible for the product is, in the first instance, the one who sold it to you. However, if the seller can prove that all reasonable precautions were taken and all due diligence was shown to ensure the sale of safe food, then the responsibility may transfer to the supplier or manufacturer. If, for example, a consumer discovered a foreign object in a can or other sealed container, it would be better to bypass the seller, and approach the manufacturer direct. For own brand products you should contact the address on the product label. Your local council office can advise you and may investigate the matter on your behalf. They have the power to prosecute in the case of a serious offence.

Q: Penalties – what happens to offenders who sell dangerous food?

A: For serious offences for example rendering food injurious to health, there is a maximum prison sentence of six months and/or a fine of £20,000 if dealt with by the Magistrates Court. For very serious offences tried in the Crown Court a maximum sentence of two years imprisonment and/or an unlimited fine may be imposed.

Q: What are date marks?

A: There are three forms of date marks. They are 'use by', 'best before' and 'display until'. The 'use by' and 'best before' dates indicate to the consumer the life expectancy of the food providing that it is stored under the recommended conditions. 'Display until' is an instruction to the retailer.

If any special instructions are required for storage these will be given on the package for example, 'Keep Refrigerated' or 'Store in a cool, dry place', and should be followed.

Q: What is a 'use by' date?

A: A 'use by' date is an **instruction** to the consumer of the period during which a product will be safe to use if kept in accordance with the manufacturer's instructions. **Food should not be used beyond its 'use by' date.** Foods with a 'use by' date should be used on or before the date given, for example, a product labelled 'use by' 24 August should be used before midnight on the 24 August.

It is illegal to sell food beyond its 'use by' date.

Q: What is a 'best before' date?

A: A 'best before' date is an **indication** to the consumer of the period during which a product will be in its best condition, if kept in accordance with the manufacturer's instructions. 'Best before' dates are often given as day/month/year i.e. 11/12/96 or 11 Dec 96. However, if the product has a shelf life of less than three months the year may be omitted. Alternatively the label may read 'Best before end' in such cases the day may be omitted and only the month and year given. For example 'Best before end Dec 96'.

Once a 'best before' date has expired the product may still be fit for consumption but may no longer be at its best, for example, cakes may be stale or biscuits soggy. The Food Safety Advisory Centre would recommend that food should be checked, to ensure that it is still wholesome, before consuming a product beyond its 'best before' date. For example, stale bread may be eaten providing it is not affected by mould, similarly butter that has passed its 'best before' date but has not gone rancid may still be edible. If there is any doubt concerning its condition, the food should not be consumed.

Q: What is a 'display until' date?

A: A 'display until' date is used primarily on foods that do not legally require a date mark, and is used by the retail store staff to indicate the period in which the product should be offered for sale. The most common use of this date code is on fresh produce, where, providing the food has been well stored, there is no health risk if consumed after the 'display until' date.

There is no legal requirement for this type of date code, it is purely for control purposes within the retail premise. A 'display until' date may occasionally be used in conjunction with a 'use by' date; in such cases consumers should take note of the 'use by' date.

Q: Who decides if a 'best before' or a 'use by' date is on a product?

A: Foods which are highly perishable and may present a risk to human health if consumed beyond that date are labelled 'use by'. Most other foods will have a 'best before' date. Foods which should be refrigerated such as prepared desserts, prepared salads, ready meals, cooked meats, paté, soft cheese or foods which contain spoilage bacteria such as poultry, fish and fresh meat, all have a typically short shelf life and so are likely to have a 'use by' date. The length of time given before the date expires is based on the manufacturers knowledge of the food working to MAFF guidelines and the food's potential life if stored under the recommended conditions. If the actual conditions of storage are different to those recommended, the date is no longer valid, for example a fresh pizza that is frozen before its 'use by' date has expired, may still be safe after the date given. However, a similar pizza stored outside the refrigerator for more than an hour on a warm day will perish before the date mark given.

Q: Do all foods require a date mark?

A: Certain foods are still exempt from the date mark system. These include:
▷ Most alcoholic drinks, with the exception of beer.
▷ Chewing Gum and similar products.
▷ Sugar and confectionery consisting almost solely of flavoured or coloured sugars.
▷ Cooking or table salt.
▷ Vinegar.
▷ Fresh fruit and vegetables which are not peeled or cut into pieces.
▷ Some baked goods such as bread and cakes which are sold fresh and will become stale before they pose a risk.
▷ Ice Cream and ice lollies in individual portions.

Q: What about foods that are in the store cupboard that have not got a date mark?

A: Some products were exempt from date marking until 20 June 1992. These include: Deep frozen food, cheese which is intended to ripen completely or partly in its packaging, foods with a long shelf life such as dried or canned foods.

If you have any of these products in your store without a date mark they will have been produced before June 1992, and may now be past their best. We would recommend that you check the recommended shelf life for these products given in Chapter IV.

Q: Are the date marks still valid once the packaging is open?

A: No. Once the food packaging is open the conditions of storage change and the food may not keep for the same length of time. Some products give a recommendation to consume within X number of days of opening; for example vacuum packed meat may state best before 12 September, use within two days of opening. Other products such as dried soups may give instructions to use the entire contents of the packet on opening.

Q: Does the Food Safety Act apply to 'eating out'?

A: Yes. The law covers the sale of all food. The main offences are the sale or intention to sell food that: is unfit for human consumption, has been rendered injurious to health, is so contaminated that it would be unreasonable to expect people to eat it, or is falsely/misleadingly presented or labelled.

It is also an offence to sell food that is not of the nature, substance or quality demanded by the purchaser. If you have any reason to be concerned about any restaurant or food outlet you would be best advised to contact an Environmental Health Officer.

Q: Does the law affect charity events such as church suppers and school fêtes?

A: All food businesses must register with their local authority. There will be no charge for registration and a local authority will not be able to refuse registration. If charity events are being run on a regular basis the organisers should contact their authority to register. Similarly, if an event is being held over several consecutive days it must also be registered. One-off events such as a harvest supper need not be registered but if you are in any doubt contact your Environmental Health Department. The Environmental Health Officer may also be able to give assistance and make recommendations on how best to prepare and store large quantities of food for such functions.

Q: Does the law ensure that food handlers are trained?

A: There is provision under the Food Safety Act to make training compulsory although this has not been enforced to date. It is recommended, however, that people who handle food be trained to an appropriate level of food hygiene, so that they understand the principles of food safety and sanitation.

FSAC FUNDED RESEARCH

Since 1990, the Food Safety Advisory Centre has funded basic public interest research work in food safety which has been carried out by a number of research organisations in the UK. Each of the projects examined an area where more scientific knowledge was required. These areas were identified by the Advisory Panel.

A number of these projects are now complete.

CLOSTRIDIUM BOTULINUM STUDY

Concern has been raised that the practice of packing goods in vacuum or modified atmosphere packs may enhance the growth of **Clostridium botulinum**. **Clostridium botulinum** is an anaerobic bacterium, which means that it grows only in the absence of air. Some **Clostridium botulinum** are also capable of growth and toxin production at cold temperatures, such as under refrigerated conditions.

The FSAC therefore financed a study, conducted by the Leatherhead Food Research Association, to investigate the incidence and growth of **Clostridium botulinum** in vacuum packed and atmosphere controlled foods. The study also investigated the production of botulinum toxin in these foods.When commercially produced vacuum packed foods and modified atmosphere packs were examined for the presence of **Clostridium botulinum**, no positive samples were found. The research organisation concluded that the incidence of **Clostridium botulinum** in modified atmosphere or vacuum packed foods stored under refrigerated conditions is rare. When foods deliberately inoculated with **Clostridium botulinum** were packed in the same way, it was found that production of toxin could occur within one week at temperatures as low as 10 degrees Celsius. However, if the shelf life of the product is observed and products are stored at temperatures not exceeding 10 degrees Celsius, toxin production seems unlikely to occur.

While these results indicate that we cannot be complacent about handling food, they are also reassuring because foods purchased from a reputable organisation are very unlikely to contain **Clostridium botulinum**.

The study has confirmed the importance of using foods before the expiry date on the pack and of storing under refrigerated conditions (5 degrees Celsius or less).

CAMPYLOBACTER JEJUNI STUDY

Campylobacter jejuni is the most frequently reported cause of food and water borne diarrhoea in Britain. A FSAC sponsored study conducted by the Public Health Laboratory Service in Exeter, investigated the incidence of **Campylobacter jejuni** in sliced cooked meats and cooked poultry.

The results of the study showed that the prevalence of **Campylobacter jejuni** contamination of cooked meat products is low.

A total of 541 samples of sliced cooked meat, eight samples of pâté and 134 samples of cooked chicken portions were examined for the presence of campylobacters. Only one sample of sliced cooked turkey breast gave any indication of containing **Campylobacter jejuni**. This however was not confirmed in further tests. In all other samples no campylobacter were found.

LISTERIA MONOCYTOGENES STUDY 1

The FSAC funded a project, at the Agricultural Food Research Council, Institute of Food Research, Reading, to investigate the factors that affect the growth and survival of **Listeria monocytogenes** in soft cheese.

The temperature of storage was shown to be a significant factor in the rate of growth of **Listeria monocytogenes** in soft mould ripened cheese. Storage at low temperatures was shown to inhibit but not prevent its growth.

> Significant growth was shown to take place in cheese of the following type:- Cambozola, French Brie, English Brie, Blue Lymeswold, White Lymeswold, French Camembert and Brie with herbs. These findings reinforce the advice of the Chief Medical Officer that these cheeses should be avoided by those individuals in an 'at risk' category (see chapter I).
>
> Little growth occurred in Blue and White Stilton, Mycella, Chaume and full fat soft cheese with garlic and herbs. These cheeses are not considered to be high risk foods and may be consumed by those in 'at risk' groups provided that they have been handled and stored correctly and the use by date is observed.

The project also examined a batch of soft Camembert cheese produced with milk deliberately inoculated with **Listeria monocytogenes**. It was found that the **Listeria monocytogenes** was present in the cheese. The rate of growth of **Listeria monocytogenes** was shown to be more rapid at the surface of the cheese than at the centre. A possible explanation for this is that favourable conditions are created by the mould rind at the surface of the cheese. The mould will naturally break down some of the proteins in the cheese milk enabling the **Listeria monocytogenes** to utilise this food source and flourish.

> The survival of **Listeria monocytogenes** under most conditions confirms the need for those in 'at risk' groups to avoid products that are made with unpasteurised milk which may be contaminated with **Listeria monocytogenes**. This study confirms that consumers in 'at risk' groups should be aware of the need to avoid all soft mould ripened cheeses. In addition all consumers should

store cheese or hard mould ripened cheeses under refrigerated conditions (5 degrees Celsius or less) in order to keep any risk to a minimum and consume by the use by date.

LISTERIA MONOCYTOENES STUDY 2

The FSAC partly financed a study conducted jointly by the Department of Microbiology at the University of Leicester and the Department of Obstetrics at the Royal Infirmary in Leicester. This study was conducted shortly after the warning given by the Chief Medical Officer, Department of Health, on the consumption of certain soft cheeses and pâté.

The project investigated the incidence of vaginal and faecal carriage of listeriae in 703 women attending the ante-natal clinic and 162 women attending the gynaecological clinic at Leicester Royal Infirmary.

No vaginal carriage and an extremely low rate of faecal carriage was detected. These unexpected findings are probably the result of improved processes and the reaction of the public to the Department of Health warning to 'at risk' groups.

The respondents were chosen at random to complete a follow-on questionnaire. The results showed that over 90% of the respondents had heard of **Listeria**, and less than 5% had consumed Brie or Camembert cheese during pregnancy. Of those that did not consume the cheese, over 50% had stopped eating the cheese as a result of advice from the Department of Health.

A small percentage (30%) had actively stopped eating pâté but less than 10% of respondents had eaten this product during pregnancy.

No significant trends were noted with regard to the consumption of raw vegetables, coleslaw or cook-chill products.

None of the respondents had drunk unpasteurised milk.

LISTERIA MONOCYTOGENES STUDY 3

The FSAC supported researchers at the Moredun Research Institute in Edinburgh to investigate the sources of Listeria in animals using a new technique known as Pyrolysis Mass Spectrometry (PyMS). PyMS allows the analysis of large numbers of veterinary samples in order to identify how different strains of **Listeria** are related to each other.

Using this technique the type of strain causing the disease in an animal, could be identified with strains in the environment and so determine the possible source of infection.

The study showed that during the infection of an animal often more than one strain is present at any one time.

Although silage feeding has long been suspected as a cause of listeriosis, the study found no direct link between strains and disease in animals.

AEROMONAS AND YERSINIA STUDY

Campden Food and Drink Research Association was funded by the FSAC to investigate the contamination of retail food samples. This survey looked specifically for two particular genera **Aeromonas** and **Yersinia**.

During the 1970's and 1980's concern was raised about two known pathogens **Aeromonas hydrophila** and **Yersinia enterocolotica.** One of the major problems with these bacteria that, like **Listeria**, they can both grow and multiply at refrigeration temperature.

The study did find a significant incidence of **Yersinia** in chopped vegetables. This may refect the increased surface area of the vegetables compared to that of the unprepared individual ingredients.

The study found the incidence of **Aeromonas** and **Yersinia** species in retail foods to be lower than in previous published studies.

One possible explanation was that the greater awareness of **Listeria** has led to increased care with product handling after production and so a concurrent reduction in the presence of other bacteria.

This work supports the fact that consumers should be constantly aware of the need to keep perishable food well refrigerated to limit the rate of growth of pathogens and to wash salad vegetables thoroughly in cold running water before serving.

SALMONELLA STUDY

The FSAC sponsored a study, conducted by the Department of Applied Biochemistry and Food Science at the University of Nottingham, to investigate the possibility of tracking the source of **Salmonella** induced food borne illness to the original food responsible. Over 100 individuals with identified food borne illness took part in a comprehensive interview and suspected food samples were taken where possible.

Fifty of the cases proved to be **Salmonella** infections. In four of the cases microbiological or molecular evidence linked the patients to the source of infection. In another 41 of the cases the source of the infection could be identified with varying degrees of confidence and in five cases the source infection remained obscure.

The sources of **Salmonella** infections implicated were:-
Eggs – 16 cases
Cross-contamination from uncooked chicken – 4 cases
Take-away sandwiches – 3 cases
Take-away sausage rolls – 1 case
Liver – 1 case
Pre-cooked chicken – 1 case
Corned beef sandwich – 1 case
Handling reptilian pets – 2 cases

This study suggests that both raw and lightly cooked eggs, take-away foods, pre-cooked foods and cross-contamination from raw poultry are the most likely sources of infection in sporadic cases of salmonellosis.

The study also highlighted the risk of contracting a **Salmonella** infection from non-food sources, in particular, reptilian pets. Young children are particularly at risk in this respect.

In addition a 12 month survey was conducted to establish the **Salmonella** contamination rates of retail chicken. No significant difference between the levels of contamination of fresh supermarket chicken, frozen supermarket chicken and chicken purchased from butcher shops/market stalls.

The results did, however, indicate that the meat from the thigh, wing or leg portions were less likely to be contaminated with **Salmonella** than breast portions or whole chicken.

When compared to other studies the results indicate a considerably reduced level of contamination of chicken meat. However, a high proportion of the positive samples were contaminated with **Salmonella enteritidis**, suggesting that this particular organism is both an ongoing and increasing problem within the industry. The increase in the number of reported cases of salmonellosis for the UK in 1992 confirm this trend.

This work again supports the fact the consumers should be aware of the possible presence of **Salmonella** in raw poultry and, as with all raw meat, should ensure that it is hygienically prepared and thoroughly cooked. It is also important to avoid using the same equipment to prepare raw food (particularly raw poultry) and cooked products. Any chopping boards, knives etc used in the preparation of raw meat should be thoroughly washed and cleaned before use in preparation of any other food.

Consumers should also avoid eating raw eggs or dishes containing raw eggs and to be absolutely safe should follow the Chief Medical Officer of Health's advice and only eat well cooked eggs (for example hard boiled).

GLOSSARY

Abdomen	(The cavity of) the lower part of the body trunk.
Additives	Substances that are added (often in quite small amounts) to food products but which perform an important function such as preserving or sweetening the product.
Aeromonas hydrophila	A pathogenic species of bacteria belonging to the family *Aeromonas*.
Aflatoxins	Any number of poisons produced by moulds.
Agrichemicals	Chemicals used for agricultural purposes, for example fertilisers or pesticides.
Agricultural practices	Any activity performed in the production of food on farms and plantations.
Alzheimer's Disease	A fatal form of dementia.
Ambient room temperature	The normal environmental temperature found in a room (room temperature in a kitchen is often about 20-25 degrees Celsius).
Amino acids	The chief components (building blocks) of proteins.
Amylase	Any of several enzymes (biological catalysts) that convert starch or glycogen to simple sugars.
Antibiotic	Substance produced by a microorganism that in dilute solution has the ability to prevent or inhibit the growth of other microorganisms.
Antiseptic	A substance that kills or inhibits microbial growth but does not damage human tissue.
Anti-toxin	Serum containing an antibody capable of neutralising a specific poison.
At risk groups	Those individuals who are most susceptible to food poisoning (see Chapter 1).

Bacillus cereus	A bacterium that is capable of producing a toxin which may bring about food poisoning.
Bacterium	Any of a group of single celled, microscopic life forms, that live in soil, water, organic matter or the bodies of plants and animals. Some of them can cause disease.

'Best before' date	A best before date is an indication to the consumer of the period during which a product will be in its best condition, if kept in accordance with the manufacturer's instructions.
Botulism	Acute, sometimes fatal food poisoning caused by *Clostridium botulinum* in (preserved) food.
Bovine	Like an ox or cow.
BSE	Bovine Spongiform Encephalopathy (Mad Cow Disease), a slowly progressive and ultimately fatal nervous disorder of cattle.
BST	Bovine Somatotropin, a protein hormone produced by the pituitary gland which occurs naturally in all milk of dairy cows.

C

Campylobacteriosis	Infectious disease caused by the group of bacteria *Campylobacter eg. Campylobacter jejuni (C. jejuni)*.
Carbohydrate	A variety of compounds consisting of carbon, hydrogen and oxygen with the ratio of hydrogen to oxygen being two to one; for example sugars, starches and cellulose.
Carcinogens	Substances producing cancer.
Carrier	A bearer who continually releases infective organisms but does not show symptoms of disease.
Chromosomes	Thread-like structures that occur in the nuclei of living cells. Each chromosome is composed of many thousands of genes.
Chymosin	A coagulent used in cheese production, this enzyme is found in rennet or can be derived from genetically modified fungus.
Clostridium botulinum (*C. botulinum*)	Causes botulism by producing a toxin in food.
Cold spots	Areas of food that are not heated properly. These are most common in foods cooked in bulk or foods that cannot be stirred. This may occur in microwave ovens due to an area not being reached by microwaves (like a blind spot). This will lead to cold spots in the food if adequate standing times are not observed or if the food is not repositioned.
Colony	A population of microbial cells growing on a solid medium arising from one original cell.

Contamination — The introduction of an unwholesome substance to food.

Cross-contamination — The transfer of a substance (eg. microorganisms) from one distinct area to another; this may be achieved by direct contact between the two areas or by use of a vector.

D

Diarrhoea — Abnormally frequent intestinal evacuations often with more or less fluid faeces.

Disinfectant — An agent that kills microorganisms but may also be harmful to human tissue.

DNA — Deoxyribonucleic acid, a complex chemical material responsible for storing the genetic code, found in chromosomes and some viruses.

E

Ecological — Concerned with the relationship of living organisms and their environment.

Endemic — Regularly occurring in.

Environmental Health Officer — The enforcement officer at local government level, whose responsibilities cover public health matters such as the hygiene of food premises and food safety.

Enzymes — Proteins that act as catalysts, aiding or facilitating biological functions.

Epidemiology — Studies that deal with the incidence, distribution and control of disease in a population.

Epizootic — An animal disease that affects a large number of animals in an area simultaneously.

Escherichia coli (E. coli) — A group of bacteria, strains of which are capable of causing food poisoning.

F

Faecal pollution — Contamination of a substance (eg. water or food) due to bodily waste. (Faeces)

Faeces — Bodily waste of the intestines excreted through the anus.

Fat — Any of a number of compounds which are made up of carbon, hydrogen and oxygen. The term fat also includes oils.

Food borne gastroentertis — Irritation of the stomach and intestines caused by an agent (eg. bacteria) carried in food.

Food chain	The process of events from production of food through to its consumption.
Food intoxication	The presence of a toxic substance in food.
Food poisoning	An acute gastrointestinal disorder caused by the toxic products of bacteria or by chemical residues in food.
Food processing	Any operation performed on food to alter its nature, often with the purpose of preserving the food or rendering it safe to eat (eg. freezing or cooking).
Foreign body	Any object that is undesirable and not normally present in a food eg. glass in milk or a caterpillar in frozen peas.

G

Gastroenteritis	Irritation of the stomach and intestines.
Genes	A unit of a chromosome which controls individual inherited characteristics. Genes are composed of DNA.
Germination	The beginning of development and growth from a seed or spore.
Germs	The common name given to bacteria, moulds, yeast and viruses.
Gut	A term given broadly to include the stomach and intestinal tract.

H

Heat transfer	The movement of heat from one area to another eg. conduction of heat from a pan base into the food on the inside.
Homeopathic drugs	Minute doses of drugs used for the treatment of a disease, which would if given to a healthy individual produce symptoms of the disease.
Hormone	A product of living cells that usually circulates in body fluids and produces a specific effect on a target group of cells.
Host	An organism capable of supporting the growth of a virus of a parasite.
Hygiene	The establishment of cleanliness and conditions conducive to the maintenance of health.

I

Immune-suppressed	Individuals who have a reduced resistance to infection, for example those who are undergoing chemotherapy.

Incubation period	The period between infection by a disease causing agent and the manifestation of the symptoms.
Infection	Growth of an organism within the body.
Intestinal tract	The tubular part of the alimentary canal that extends from the stomach to the anus.

L

Lactose	Sugar in milk.
Listeriosis	The disease caused by the bacterium *Listeria monocytogenes*.
Lymph glands	Tissue responsible for the production of white blood cells.

M

MAFF	Ministry of Agriculture, Fisheries and Food.
Magnetron	The device that generates microwaves in a microwave oven.
Malnourishment	Poor quality diet.
Mastitis	Inflammation of the breast or udder usually caused by infection, for example, listerial mastitis would be caused by infection of the mammary gland by *Listeria monocytogenes*.
Meningitis	Bacterial fungal or viral inflammation of membranes that envelope the brain and spinal cord.
Metabolites	Products required for, or produced by, biochemical reactions in cells in the body.
Microbial Contamination	Contamination by microorganisms.
Microbial load	The number and type of microorganisms in food.
Microorganisms	Living organisms of microscopic size, the three main categories are bacteria, moulds and yeast.
Microwave	Electromagnetic waves with very short wave lengths.
Microwave oven	An oven in which food is cooked by heat produced as a result of the interaction between penetrating microwaves and the molecules in the food.
Migrate	The ability for a substance to move from one distinct area to another.
Monoculture	The cultivation of a single crop.

Moulds	A group of microorganisms with a fuzzy cotton wool appearance.
Mycotoxins	Toxic substances produced by a mould or fungus.

N

Nausea	Feeling of discomfort in the stomach accompanied by headache and distaste of food.

O

Organism	A living being.
Outbreak of food poisoning	Where two or more persons who are associated in time and/or place show symptoms of food poisoning.

P

Parasite	An organism that lives on or off another living organism (the host) to the benefit of the parasite and the detriment of the host.
Pasteurisation	A process of applying mild heat to reduce the number of microorganisms present in a substance that is itself heat sensitive eg. pasteurised milk.
Pathogens	An organism capable of inflicting damage upon a host it infects.
Patulin	A mycotoxin produced by the action of certain moulds on soft fruit.
Pesticides	A substance that kills undesirable organisms eg. Fungicides kill moulds and fungi.
Plasticiser	An additive added to plastics to give them a flexible and often clingy quality.
Poison	Any substance that is destructive and harmful to an organism, which may kill or injure due to its chemical nature.
Protein	A group of complex substances made up of carbon, hydrogen, oxygen and nitrogen often in combination with phosphorous and sulphur. The component units of proteins are amino acids.

R

Rendering	Processing offal and animal carcasses to make meat and bone meal for animal feed.

Rennet	An extract containing the enzyme chymosin, traditionally taken from a calf's fourth stomach and used to curdle milk for cheese production.
Ruminant	A group of hoofed mammals including cattle, sheep, giraffes and camels that chew the cud and have a complex three or four chambered stomach.

S

Salivation	The production of saliva.
Salmonella	A family of bacteria causing diseases (salmonellosis) including food poisoning in warm blooded animals.
Salmonella enteritidis (*S. enteritidis*)	A species of bacteria belonging to the family *Salmonella*.
Shelf life	The shelf life of a product is the period of time over which any particular food product can be expected to last under its recommended conditions of storage.
Solanine	Bitter poisonous substance found in several plants such as green potatoes.
Species	A biological class of individuals having common attributes.
Spina bifida	A defect of the spine.
Spores	The reproductive body produced by plants, moulds and some bacteria.
Staphylococcus aureus (*S. aureus*)	A species of bacteria producing toxins which bring about the symptoms of food poisoning.
Sterilisation	A treatment resulting in the death of all living organisms, including viruses in material.
Strain	A population of cells all descending from a single cell: a clone.
Symptom	Evidence or indication of disease.
Systemic	Affecting the whole body.

T

Thermometer	An instrument to determine temperature.
Thermostat	An instrument for regulating temperature (this is achieved automatically).
Toxicity	The degree of potency of a poisonous substance.

Toxoplasmosis	The disease caused by the parasitic microorganism *Toxoplasma gondii.*
Trading Standards Officer	The enforcement officer at local government level who covers commercial law such as weights and measures and the correct labelling of food products.

U

UHT	Ultra High Temperature treatment (at least 130 degrees Celsius for 1 second) used to heat treat milk or fruit juice.
Undernourishment	Lack of food.
'Use by' date	A 'Use By' date is an instruction to the consumer of the period during which a product will be safe to use if kept in accordance with the manufacturer's instructions.

V

Vector	An agent of transmission for pathogens usually an insect or other animal but may be an inert object such as a spoon or chopping board.
Veterinary Medicine	A medicine used in the treatment of animals. All medicines are subject to license under the Medicines Act.
Virology	A branch of science that deals with viruses.
Vitamin	Organic compounds that are an essential part of the diet in minute quantities.

W

World Health Organisation	An apolitical organisation dealing with health issues: Part of the United Nations.

Y

Yersinia enterocolitica	A pathogenic species of bacteria belonging to the family *Yersinia.*

INDEX

INDEX